D1034473

SECRET LIFE OF A SECRET AGENT

BY HENRY WYSHAM LANIER

SECRET LIFE OF A SECRET AGENT

HE DID NOT DIE AT MEYERLING

SECRET LIFE OF A SECRET AGENT

The Strange Training and Adventures of a Man Whose Work Was Melodrama

BY

HENRY WYSHAM LANIER

PHILADELPHIA NEW YORK

J. B. LIPPINCOTT COMPANY

LONDON TORONTO

MADE IN THE
UNITED STATES OF
AMERICA

PREFATORY NOTE

This story is true.

I have written it from long and intimate talks with the man whose extraordinary history I have tried to portray.

To meet the obvious requirement of anonymity, names have been omitted or altered. Also some non-essential facts have been deliberately twisted. But the entire effort has been to present a reality which seems to have significance.

Mr. X's life-story is not only a striking human document. The melodramatic adventures of his routine work lead directly back to the governmental mechanism which trained him and directed his undercover labors.

Possibly other people are as unaware as I was of the growth and scope of modern "military intelligence."

Of course, there have always been spies. The Israelites fleeing from Egypt sent men ahead to spy out the Promised Land. Militant early Christians named the Wednesday before Good Friday "Spy Wednesday," because on that day the Sanhedrin tried to ferret out some discreditable or fatal weakness of the disturber Jesus. The ex-army-officer convict, Vidocq, was trained by the French Government for chief of the secret police by an apprenticeship of spying on his fellow criminals. As shrewd Casanova remarked nearly two centuries ago, "the only open spies are Ambassadors."

Just as Great Britain is feverishly preparing defences against air-raids, her Under-secretary of the Home Office goes to Berlin to examine the system of air-shelters worked out by Germany—the only country from which she could fear air-raids! And it is an accepted fact that naval, military and air attachés are at the embassy mainly to gather information about the military strength and new war-making devices of the country to which they are accredited.

A short time ago a journalist described the magnificent Nazi reception to Sir Robert Vansittart, the British Permanent Under-secretary of State for Foreign Affairs. He added that all Europe's diplomats were grinning over the situation–since everybody knew that Sir Robert was really the alert head of his country's Secret Service, spending $1,250,000 each year to catch and jail spies, chiefly German ones.

War-time spies are shot by the enemy and then have statues erected to them by their own people.

But I fancy few of us realize what a web of stealthy espionage is being woven daily all about us, even in piping times of peace. Woven by individuals, corporations, governments. Woven frequently with craft, violence and blood. Woven in the name of self-preservation, business prosperity, a "holy" cause, patriotism. Woven eagerly, skilfully, ruthlessly even as you read these lines.

Efficient business men have often financed the theft of trade secrets from business rivals. Management spies on labor, unions on the bosses. Every post-office building erected in these United States must have a concealed spy-chamber from which alert inspectors can at all times secretly overlook patrons and workers. In some lines of crime the "stool-pigeon" is the main instrument in the hands of our police departments. In a great American city, an entire floor in a tall building is given over to the busy activities of a foreign power's intelligence bureau, earnestly gathering and collating a vast mass of facts, documents, plans, maps and photographs—such as every great nation's war chiefs now demand of every other country.

This monstrous umbrageous growth of military Information is almost entirely a product of the last century.

Napoleon's military intelligence department was a single man, Bacler d'Albe, a skilled cartographer. The conqueror of Europe planned his miraculous victories lying flat on his belly, stretched out over large-scale maps, compass in hand; by his side was Colonel d'Albe, ready to furnish all the exact knowledge he had gathered, through a few such agents as Schulmeister the Alsatian smuggler, about every detail of topography, the particular enemy regiments facing them, the generals, and so on.

Judged by results, that worked rather well. But to-day there are at least seven great organizations, each collecting, with fanatical zeal and by any methods necessary, a prodigious corpus of Information, about the strengths and weaknesses and new inventions of every other nation.

That is a picture which makes one think.

This factual story shows one section of that Machine in action.

H. W. L.

CONTENTS

CONTENTS

SECRET LIFE OF A SECRET AGENT

INTRODUCTORY

For more than quarter of a century I lied, and stole, and deceived, and bribed, and killed men suddenly and ruthlessly—all in doing my everyday job.

Not once did my conscience reproach me. Nor does it now. Rather do I feel that I have "deserved well of my country." The responsibility was not mine, but that of the leaders of that country I served to the utmost of my ability.

I realize now I have been necessarily a solitary. Nothing stirs me violently. There is no man or woman in the whole world to whom I can talk freely of anything I know at first hand or feel deeply.

A secret agent must live without friends, without love, without excitements, without even enthusiasms. Only when these artistic irregularities are completely polished off from his personality does he become the perfect instrument for his task.

He must work tirelessly with his inexorable

trainers to make of himself one of those accurate, complicated, unfeeling "business machines," of which your country in particular has developed so various and marvellous a supply for your business offices. They do everything—except think. The directing mind can use them (from universal typewriter to the most complex tabulating, or industrial scales mechanisms), use them to write a "poison pen" letter that may assassinate some sensitive, innocent woman, or to make a false statement that may ruin a disliked, proud and honorable man—just as easily as for their admirable legitimate purposes.

Only when you have attained that supreme emotionless control are you a fit instrument to perform that tortuous, underground work which Authority in every land deems its lawful occasions.

These High Ones must consider the aims of these activities important: they are eager, even in untroubled times, to risk a dozen human lives a day to carry them out.

It is they, the Brass Hats, who "have ze information." We agents know nothing of the reason why, what went before our stealthy acts, or what followed from our success.

I say success. For we who remain in the Service are invariably successful. Those who failed have as a rule retired permanently into a snug, six-foot wooden house. Or perhaps the same length of unmarked earth.

You think the old man grows a bit melodramatic?

I don't know about that. I read that the original Greek "melodrama" was a play with exciting incidents and musical accompaniments.

Anyhow, I have lived what I take people to mean by "melodrama," day and night, for over thirty years. That is quite long enough to form a habit.

And I wonder at times if your superior Intellectual, who scorns the "untruth" and "bad art" of melodrama, may not be merely ignorant of those segments of everyday life where the only normal existence *is* melodrama.

Among these the Secret Agent's work surely occupies a chief place.

Looking at all that from my present perspective, I find I have ideas about it. Hazy, formless ideas. Possibly it is because of those mental stirrings that I am now willing to relate a plain tale of what I have experienced.

CHAPTER I

A Significant Beginning

"But, Marie, this is absurd, unhuman, monstrous."

The young mother, lying in bed with her baby beside her, smiled painfully.

"You can call it anything you like, sister. Names can't alter the fact that it's part of my life."

"But what possible excuse can your husband offer for behaving in so unheard-of a manner?"

"Excuse! The Captain! My dear, those words come from two different languages, so unrelated you can't use them intelligibly in the same sentence."

"Still– What is in the man's mind?"

"You really want to know?"

"Yes. It seems positively insane. Yet one wants the satisfaction of understanding the workings of such a twisted brain."

"Oh, there is no twist. It is all beautifully straight and logical."

"Logical!"

"Precisely."

"I see no logic or common sense in it."

"That's because you don't accept his premise."

"And what is that, pray?"

"To begin with, the Captain bulks so commandingly in the Captain's mind, no room is left there for anyone or anything else—except as these minor details affect him."

"Of course I've always known, poor Marie, that he was a colossal egotist."

"Well, he has reasons: one of his ancestors fought in the First Crusade."

"There are moments when I wish the Saracens had taken that ancestor prisoner and kept him out there forever."

"They didn't. He came home and begat a proud son. That one begat a prouder. That has been going on for a thousand years."

"It seems like a lot of time and labor—to produce This."

"So my Lord and Master started as a Person of Importance. And all his life he has built up that importance in every possible way."

"Well, I hear he is really brilliant in his profession. He'll be a General some day."

"No doubt. I wonder what I and the children will be—some day."

"You poor child! You don't love him at all any more, do you?"

A wave of color flushed the pale cheeks of the woman lying in the great bed whose hangings displayed a coat-of-arms.

"We won't discuss that, please, my sister."

"I can see the picture you draw. And after all, one must grant he has succeeded in that effort. He is a success, a distinguished officer in the army."

"Ah, yes, no one could fail to be aware of that. Least of all his family."

"I realize he is a frightful martinet. The Major says all his subordinates shake in their shoes when he comes in sight."

"His subordinates, yes. No doubt they tremble. Yet the army regulations protect them. There are no rules, no limits in the Captain's home, except those he sets up."

"You will make me cry. It is really frightful."

"I sometimes think—" said Marie.

"What?"

"That he is like that terrible Yahveh of the Old Testament: he can only be happy when all around him cower in fright at the sound of his voice."

For the first time emotion broke through her unnatural restraint. Its intensity alarmed her sister.

"It is frightful," she repeated. "Frightful. Yet, even now, I don't see—"

"Why, it all follows most naturally. Such a man, representing so long a procession of noble ancestors —you admit he must have a son to carry on the glorious Name."

"Yes, but that is the very point. Here is that baby son finally. Yet—"

"Ah, how little you understand the General-that-is-to-be."

"What *do* you mean?"

"First, six years ago, there came Maryse. A girl,

you see. Not a son to perpetuate the Name. That was a shocking failure."

"Yes, but gracious heavens, even admitting that stupid point of view, the responsibility for the failure, as you call it, was surely a divided one."

"I said you had not yet grasped the a b c of the Captain. Failure always belongs to the other person. In himself there is no such possibility."

"You really mean to tell me he blamed you for *that?*"

"Completely. Coldly. Bitterly. The one personal mistake he might perhaps admit—and that only to me—was a mistake on his part in choosing me to produce this necessary son for him."

"Merciful Virgin!"

"Three years I bore the brunt of his stern displeasure over that shameful error. I tell you, you can't imagine what it has been, living with that cold, dark, locked-up, outraged disapproval. Then the time came when I might possibly redeem myself by performing my primary duty. Merely doing the one thing a woman is fit for, you understand. The answer to that was—little Marthe. Another girl! Imagine."

"You poor darling. I never dreamed of this."

"From that time on I was completely inadequate, untrustworthy, negligible if not actually criminal."

"What a demon of a man!"

"And of course now, with a baby son beside me, I must not be allowed to suppose that I am re-established in his eyes, merely because I have succeeded—once in three times."

"It is incredible."

"Therefore he does not choose to let the event assume undue importance. When he is ready, he will inspect the tardy boy. He wishes me to understand clearly that he may possibly not approve of him after all."

"You really mean—after three weeks—"

"I have not seen him. He has not found it worth while to look at his son."

"Why, the man is actually possessed of a devil."

"He is possessed of himself. Holy Father Augustin himself could not exercise that coldly superior spirit."

"This darling big boy is far too good for him. Let him stay away, I say."

"That would be too much to hope for. The day of reckoning must come. I know exactly how the runaway slave used to feel, there in the West Indies, as he crouched in the bushes, certain that sooner or later he would have to face his outraged master."

"But, Marie, this can't go on. No human being can remain normal in such a morbid atmosphere. You will have to leave him, come to us."

The other laughed bitterly. "What rights has a wife? Would the family council back me in such a scandal? To leave my noble and distinguished husband for such petty, fanciful, feminine reasons! Wouldn't Father Benoit probably threaten me with excommunication if I didn't return at once to my Duty?"

"I'm afraid you're right. But there must be some—"

She stopped short as a little girl of six ran into the room, round-eyed.

"Oh, Mother! Mother!" she panted. "Father is here. And I think–"

All three sat silent as a harsh, angry voice was heard below.

"Albert was cleaning," whispered the child. "He had on a dirty old coat when he went to open the door. I knew Father would be very angry."

"Never mind, Maryse. Everything will be all right. See–the baby is smiling at you."

"Oh, Mother, he knows me. He knows me! Isn't he too darling!"

She bent over the laughing, crowing infant–then straightened up suddenly. For a moment she stood listening.

"Oh, Mother!" she whispered. "He's coming!"

Her face and tone expressed complete terror.

Marie and her sister looked at each other. Then the young mother raised the baby to her breast, and strove to look unconcerned.

Her sister made a feminine effort: "I think it's

remarkable, Marie, the way that child gains. He hasn't had a single set-back since he was born."

"No, he's as good as gold."

She looked up with a poor pretence of naturalness as a tall figure strode into the room.

The Captain was in dress uniform. Tall and erect, he seemed to fill the room with scarlet and gold and burnished metal. Also with something else less glittering.

Without a word he came close to the bed, looked down at the pink scrap of humanity lying against its mother's arm.

There was not the slightest softening of his cold, military severity. His eyes examined the infant with much the same sceptical, impersonal judgment he would have applied to a new cavalry horse or a company of recruits.

The child looked up at him. It was not smiling now.

The Captain frowned.

Immediately the baby burst into loud wailing. The mother caught it closer, tried to soothe it. But some subtle emotional vibration had reached the baby: it cried with that complete abandonment of childhood, which knows nothing beyond the moment's convulsive fear and distress.

The Captain continued to inspect it, with a remoteness changing to active disgust.

"He will never make a real soldier, that one," he stated with finality.

And turning, he marched out of the room.

Both women were crying quietly now. And the little girl was breathless with the effort to strangle her sobs.

That small tragi-comedy is the only incident in this narrative which is not told from my own recollection.

Obviously it came to me from the older people present.

I am sure it did happen. For it was a perfect miniature expression of our family life for the next twenty years.

Except in one respect—the utterance by my mother of her suppressed feelings. During all those long years I can recall only one case where she opposed her lord and master openly in anything. Then it was a harsh injustice to one of my sisters which aroused her protest; and for weeks afterward she was made to feel the enormity of this crime against nature.

For my father required from all about him the public acknowledgment that he was the infallible Head, in whom lay all final authority.

And I can see now how vital an influence this relation was in making me what I became.

CHAPTER II

The Army Gallops

I WAS ALONE, AS USUAL, A SOLEMN LITTLE boy of five. Already I knew it was probably wiser not to play with my sisters unless we were safely by ourselves. There were no other boys to play with. So the big box of lead soldiers, practically my only toys, were highly important, even if not precisely gay.

Indeed I hardly missed gaiety, never having known it.

The room was plain and bare, befitting a soldier's son in a garrison town. There was a rigorous exclusion of any artistic grace, or ease, or sentimental appeal, which might evoke some deplorable strain of Capuan softness in a childish mind. The very earliest impressions must be focussed upon life's realities and the true reason for being.

From the very beginning, Discipline. Discipline, utter subjection to Authority. The only sure foundation for an orderly world. The basis of the Army itself.

So the afternoon sun, striking through the west windows, fell upon two of the three pictures which symbolized this controlling idea in dramatic action. They were color engravings, stirring enough for a young male animal, moved by swift activity; for they represented three famous cavalry onslaughts.

One pictured that epic Charge of the Light Brigade at Balaklava. Another was the blind dash over Alsatian hills of the cuirassiers covering the French retirement at Reichshoffen in 1870. And the third showed that supreme feat of the Bayreuth dragoons at Hohenfriedberg, when 1,500 horsemen overwhelmed twenty battalions of enemy infantry.

Quite international, you see. Impersonal, even. Simply examples that showed the glories of armies at work. Military science in its most colorful and exciting manifestation.

I noticed them particularly this day in the sunlight, because the mounted leaders looked like the awe-inspiring giant who rode up to our home at least once every day on a glossy, foam-spattered bay charger. Also some of the brilliant uniforms were similar to those in my well-stocked box.

So, with the anxious care I had already learned from rapped knuckles, I opened my wooden cantonment and lifted out horsemen, foot-soldiers and guns.

Infantry in a mob by themselves facing me. Artillery grouped uncertainly to the left. But the cavalry somehow I wanted on my side. Cavalry belonged to that huge and terrifying person who dominated everything in my world.

I managed to set them up without bending or breaking any of the slender legs. Something was wrong. This irregular group of riders did not satisfy me, gay as were the uniforms, proudly curved as were the horses' necks.

As I sat on the floor, gravely considering this, a deep voice behind me made me start:

"Sixteen of them, in one straight line, in front."

It was not necessary to look up. Anyhow, I was trembling inside, as we all did at the sound of that voice. Obediently, I began to form a line of my mounted troops.

"Each one the same distance from each other one."

The spaces were corrected a second and third time before he was content.

"Dress the line. Straight, straight. Look along it."

The line was dressed.

"Now, sixteen more behind them, exactly like the front rank."

I was nervous and clumsy, but at last it was accomplished to his satisfaction.

"Now you have a troop of cavalry instead of a mounted rabble. That is what discipline does."

Of course I could not understand that. But if "discipline" was something which pleased this awe-inspiring personage, I must try to keep hold of it.

"Put another troop in line with that one. Exactly like it. Begin at this distance."

I obeyed.

"Dress your lines. Straight. Always straight."

Presently my lead cavalry was in four precise blocks.

"That is a squadron. With a squadron, properly handled, a commander can begin to do something."

He was being very patient with me—as one trains a colt or a puppy.

"Now suppose that squadron moves forward. First at a trot, then at a gallop. Like those dragoons in the picture." He pointed to the charging Bayreuthers.

"They gallop down on all those infantrymen there. They ride knee to knee. Their line is kept as straight as it is at present—as straight as a sword. What will happen when that line hits that great mass of infantry?"

In the interest of that thought I forgot my nervous dread of doing something wrong. I looked up at him, wondering.

"This is what happens."

With a sweep of his hand the lead infantry were hurled down and aside. A jagged gap was opened up through the centre. I exclaimed in pleasure.

"That is one of the things a cavalry force is for," he said.

And with this to reflect on, he left me to my play.

But this solitary play was no longer casual and aimless. I had tasted the stimulating draught of power. With deep excitement I re-tasted and savored it as I launched my cavalry thunderbolts on those foolish, futile infantrymen, whose function was to serve as a target for my irresistible dragoons.

And the exploits of these mounted heroes were prodigious, unparalleled. After only a minimum of training, a single troop would sometimes cut an opposing battalion to pieces. If the military historians of the eighties could but have witnessed those magnificent charges, the Bayreuthers' classic victory would have been relegated to a second-rate example.

That was what it meant to be a soldier. Especially a cavalry leader.

This huge expansion of ideas and ambitions served me well a month or two later.

Thinking ourselves safe one afternoon, my sisters and I were playing hide-and-seek. The game had turned into a romp, and we were dashing about, squealing shrilly, falling over chairs, entirely given up to the breathless excitement of chase and discovery.

In the middle of the hubbub the Captain came in unexpectedly.

Each one of us stood motionless, as if frozen into the attitude of that fatal instant. It was like one of those Eastern tales where an enchanter suddenly turns a whole household of living beings to stone. That formidable figure simply stood there, without a word.

The utter silence became too much for little Annette. She began to sniffle, and a big tear rolled down each of her flushed cheeks.

"You girls can go to your rooms," announced the Captain. The three crept out guiltily.

Then he turned to my pale mother.

"Is this your idea of training my son?" he inquired.

There was no answer expected or given.

"Evidently it is time I should take the boy in hand. Send him to my quarters at ten o'clock to-morrow morning. I will have him taught to ride a horse. That will be more appropriate, I think, than romping with girls in such undisciplined disorder."

At five, a cavalry horse seems somewhat overlarge. But for the recollection of those superb charges of my lead soldiers, I might have disgraced myself by showing fear at this prospect. That would have made no difference in the event, since the Captain had spoken; but it would have subjected me to that cold contempt which was already something to be avoided at all costs. As it was, I could retire, leaving the impression that I was altogether pleased at this masculine promotion.

It proved to be even better than I had dared to hope. The old stable sergeant was a kindly yet thorough teacher. I was excited by the big, powerful horses and the swift strength I was bestriding. I learned to tumble off on the tanbark and think nothing of it—the foundation of a finished horseman's skill.

Within a year I could stick on most of the mounts like a monkey, and began to dream of reaching proficiency some day in the showy "high school" performances in which the regiment's crack riders displayed their mastery.

Presently I was turned over to the grizzled master-of-arms, given a wooden sabre almost as long as I, and started on the long training to swordsmanship. Evidently the Captain had instructed my teachers to work me hard. I would be kept at practice with sabre or foil until my arm would sink from fatigue. Then a short rest—and at it again.

Before I was nine, a sword and a saddle were as natural to me as a baseball or a tennis racquet to an American boy.

Looking back at it, I can see that even at this age I was a solitary little being.

Playmates were frowned on: it was unthinkable that a son of the noble captain should play with inferiors. And the delightful hours with my cousin Peter were too occasional to counteract the sheer fear of this autocrat who ruled my universe and who was so easily and inexplicably offended.

If a child volunteered any remark at the dinner-table, without having been addressed by the master, he or she was instantly sent away hungry. It did not take much of that to teach a small boy to keep his small ideas to himself.

Anyhow, it demanded most of one's attention to hold constantly in mind the rigid rules, laid down or unspoken, violation of which brought stern punishment.

Half a century later one recurring incident returns poignantly. That quivering child lies in bed at night after one of these constant scenes of brutal discipline. Somehow he has managed to hide his hurt at the time—not because of fear alone, but from a deep sense of helpless outrage. Now, alone in the dark, the relief of quiet, hopeless crying is inevitable. Then, presently, a white figure steals into the room. Without a word, his mother takes him in her arms. Restrained even then by the dread of arousing the ogre and calling down a fresh storm of rage, the tears of both mingle silently together.

We lived in the shadow, always dreading some new disapproval, anger, chastisement. Inevitably, all natural expression was checked. Whatever we really were could have only a mole-like, underground existence.

Naturally, I felt awkward with other people. I suppose I was subconsciously ashamed of this extraordinary subjection in which we were held. But, without realizing that, I was not easy with other boys. I did not understand them. I was sensitive about the many things they did and talked about which were a closed book to me. And, except in the case of Peter, that instinctive young expectation of making a friend, to whom one could talk freely—that would have seemed grotesque.

So my external calm had no relation to my inner feelings when my father announced one day that I was to go off to boarding-school.

"You are big enough now to begin to learn something," he announced. That pleased me. I was proud of being as tall as a boy of twelve; and this one small vanity he fostered. For he himself was over six feet.

"You will leave to-morrow for the Jesuit school where I myself got my first education. I expect you will do nothing to discredit my name there."

I said nothing. That was not expected unless a direct question were asked. As usual this was an order, an announcement of a decision by Authority.

"I have taught you to obey," said the Captain, coldly. "But there are moments when I am doubtful of your inner discipline. I shall tell the masters of this defect. They know how to treat potential insubordination."

I still kept silence.

"The Army, the Church, the State are founded on unquestioning, whole-hearted obedience. Those who cannot discipline themselves must be disciplined."

I was nine years old.

The next day, as announced, I left home for the Jesuit school.

CHAPTER III

Remote Control

Homesickness can be a really serious ailment. A sensitive boy who has always been surrounded by family love, suddenly thrown on his own responsibility among a hundred strange boys and men, sometimes suffers a sort of emotional paralysis.

Even the adults of some races are unable to make this adjustment. I have seen a young Teuton become actually ill for his native Bavaria. And it is a traditional fact that the Swiss mountaineer cannot be transplanted, except by surrounding him with a miniature reproduction of his native land. Even a jig-saw chalet may furnish the necessary illusion.

Heaven knows the new school conditions and personalities were strange and disturbing enough to me—who knew nothing and nobody outside my narrow little round. But homesickness! No. I had never known a home whose absence could produce those pangs.

Rather was there a deep, furtive hope that this might mean a temporary escape from the oppressive rule which overshadowed everything in our household. I had a momentary fancy of what it might be to live as Cousin Peter did, free, easy, natural, even giving way to impulses. Just to do what I wanted to do at that particular instant, to laugh, to break loose in the young animal play which is a growing boy's instinct. There was a timid anticipation that all sorts of pleasant things might be waiting for me in this new existence of the seminary school.

I soon discovered I had underestimated the omnipresence of our particular household Omnipotence.

Old Albert, the wrinkled man-of-all-work inherited from my grandfather, conducted me to the neighboring town.

It was a bright, sunshiny morning. The fresh wind herded fleecy lamb-clouds across the blue sky, washed clean by a night's rain.

"Be a good boy now, and obey all the rules. Then you won't get into trouble."

With this distillation of his own patient, life-long experience, rheumatic Albert turned me over to the doorkeeper—a saturnine Cerberus, whose many years of seminary watchfulness had developed sharpness of observation equal to at least nine pairs of ordinary eyes. Also an unsleeping suspicion of the worst.

He received me and my scanty belongings as he would any other consignment of supplies—with impersonal boredom and impatience.

Presently I was deposited in the little white-washed cell which was to be home for most of some succeeding years.

"Report to the Dean at once," he growled. And then, irritated at my blank look: "Over there. In his office."

As I started off I could hear his grumbling comment: "Seems like they get dumber and dumber each year."

That contempt did not trouble me. Not after living under the Captain for all my nine years.

I made my way along the bare corridors to the Dean's office. I realized this unknown personality would probably be important to my future.

He proved to be a spare little man with a high forehead, close-trimmed grey beard, and an enveloping air of utter certainty.

He asked some questions as to what I had learned at home, and nodded in approval.

"Yes, yes. Very sound preparation. As I expected. You are ready for us. And we are ready for you."

It was precisely the attitude I noticed many years later in a manufacturer, looking over a fresh shipment of raw material and finding it free from impurities and up to standard.

"I expected no less," went on the Dean. "For I know your father."

I do not know whether my sigh was audible or merely internal.

"Twenty years ago he was my pupil in Philosophy. This restless-minded modern age insists on splitting up that noble science. Soon, instead of considering the whole corpus of higher knowledge, we professors of Philosophy will be teaching metaphysics alone."

You can imagine the effect of that on a boy of nine.

"In any case, I shall always consider your father one of the most remarkable pupils I have ever had. Even then he had a passion for exact truth."

I felt a little flutter of pride at this ponderous praise. Looking back, that childish quiver of pleasure seems deeply ironic. The human ego, even though humiliated by complete domination, can still take this strange satisfaction in outside assurance that its tyrant is a superior person.

Up to this time the Dean had scarcely looked at me. He now gave me a shrewd, direct stare, searching yet impersonal.

"Your father has communicated certain things to me. I shall hope to find that his affection has overemphasized his—apprehensions."

Suddenly I was a lawbreaker before a judge. On probation. Under suspicion.

"You are destined for the Army. This school is a perfect place to give you your primary training.

For all of us who belong to the Society of Jesus are soldiers. Do you understand that?"

"I think so, sir."

"Soldiers of Holy Church. Bound together in a formal, drilled, mighty military organization, under the supreme Father General. Ready for action at any moment to defend our Order and the Church. Do you know what it is that welds us into this efficient fighting unit?"

"I think I do."

"What?"

"It is discipline, isn't it, sir?"

"Exactly. Discipline. Giving up one's own petty will and desires to become an effective part of something greater than any one man. Obedience. Holding back nothing. I see you have heard that mighty word, Discipline."

"Yes, sir."

"Never forget it. Live by it."

"Yes, sir."

"That is all for the present. Obey. Never question, even in your mind."

Well, I could understand that. And there was

nothing strange or novel in it. But it was a solemn small boy who went out from the Dean's office.

At least, no one else could have detected that he was burying a tiny, new-born hope he had been secretly nourishing—as a child buries the fledgling bird he has picked up and petted. It flutters no longer.

I realized that the fifty miles of distance, which seemed to me so vast a stretch, could not for an instant check the operation of my father's personal power. More than ever this unseen regulation seemed inescapable. It took on the aspect of destiny.

Had there been any lingering doubts as to the persistence of that remote control, they could hardly have survived the next few years.

I took my minute part at once in this smoothly running machinery.

I memorized, and listened and studied by a rigorous schedule, covering most of our waking hours. I recited, repeated parrot-like what I had retained. Exact marks for accuracy of answers and examinations, for application and conduct, accumulated on a report card—which speedily became a focus of practical and lively concern. For I learned from experience that demerits had a definite meaning when I returned home: so many produced a tongue-lashing from the household censor; one more brought a lashing with the riding-crop. Hard to say which was worse.

To be sure we had our school play-hour, but even in the occasional football and larking I could rarely forget the pressure of my personal responsibilities. It was with a sort of amazement that I watched some reckless fellows who, deliberately or thoughtlessly, broke the sacred rules—and then lied their way out, or took their punishment as an exciting adventure.

They seemed a different order of beings from this anxious youngster, myself, waking up with a start in his dormitory bed at the remembrance of some mistake or failure. Trembling at the picture of the consequences.

There were such moments when I saw against night's blackness in letters of fire those portentous words. DISCIPLINE. OBEY. NEVER QUESTION.

I might well have become completely broken

in spirit, but for the daily exercise in riding and fencing. Here I could more than hold my own with other boys of my age; and since I was already scheduled for the officers' school, I had an unusual allotment of time for this practice. Any independence of thought I reached later was built on the foundations of that physical mastery of horse and sword.

We had ten days' vacation at Easter, but I had my daily task then too, under a more exacting master than the teachers at school. The work must be completed satisfactorily before there was any thought of play.

Almost the only break came during the summer holidays. We left school for two months, July and August. And—excitement of excitements!—for three weeks of this period I was permitted to go and stay with Cousin Peter, whose family spent each summer in a country house some miles down the river.

I still had to report by post each day and present my regular completed task. But no matter. During those happy weeks I breathed the air of freedom. Peter and I romped, and rowed, looked for birds' nests, pried into everything, and compared notes on our schools and our futures.

One small piece of experimental nature-study had consequences.

We were walking past a farm to get to the river. Something stirred up the flock of fat white ducks by the pond. Their clumsy, waddling dash and the prodigious quackings made us stop to laugh and listen.

"Say," said Peter, "I wonder what would happen if you could keep those bills wide open all the time."

"Easy to find out."

"Right. Let's try it."

We drove a bunch of indignant ducks into a corner, caught them one by one, and tied a piece of stick into the mouth of each, to produce the requisite conditions for our scientific test.

The result was immense. The deafening racket that followed was most gratifying to an investigator in its positiveness.

But we had failed to visualize the publicity effect

of success. The farmer came running up; and while we escaped easily, detection was simple.

He made formal complaint. Peter and I got such a tremendous hiding that we envied those ducks in their free expression of feeling.

My cousin was violently indignant. From that day he detested my father, and spent hours in scheming out some plan to get back at him. One of these succeeded.

Peter hired a disreputable townsman to telephone our home in the middle of the night. Aroused from heavy sleep, my father stumbled to the telephone.

"You're wanted at the barracks at once, sir," exclaimed an excited voice.

"What's that? What's happened?"

"Order for immediate practice in mobilization, sir."

"What? What? How did that come? Who is this speaking?"

No answer from a dead line.

Impossible to disregard that summons. Grimly resolved to make an example of someone for the manner of notification, the Captain hurried into his clothes, roused the household, dashed to the barracks—to find the usual midnight calm.

Worst of all, there was nobody on whom to vent his wrath.

He was more furious over that than I have ever seen him, except on one memorable occasion. But so astute was Peter's plan, his utmost persistent efforts failed to discover the guilty party.

My cousin's defiant protest helped to build up in me some standard of comparison between my home conditions and those of a normal family. My uncle was far from slack: he too was of the Army. But there was ease, laughter, sympathy and quick affection in that household. A dictator makes a fatal mistake in permitting his subjects to come in contact with freedom while they are still at an impressionable age. Before they themselves know it, they are ripe for sedition.

Indeed, my dictator's alert jealousy of his prerogative must have caused him to sense possibilities of my inner revolt long before I dreamed of such a thing. I know from year to year I grew more and more silent under his discipline. I never asked for any relaxation of his most arbitrary rules. When I came home a few minutes behind schedule, I received the inevitable whipping without any attempt to justify myself. I learned to take the lashes of the hard-worked riding-crop without crying, even with a minimum of flinching.

That must have gradually aroused his suspicion. He wanted us to tremble. It was a reflection on his power that I should receive his just chastisement and not cry out.

He increased these rigors, determined to crush insubordination before it took root. And I suppose he built up powers of resistance in the white-faced boy who endured it without breaking down.

An odd happening heightened this unspoken tensity between us.

At fourteen I had a severe attack of typhoid. I was a large strong boy, already five feet, six inches tall. I came through all right, recovering my health completely—but I never grew a fraction of an inch in height after that.

Now my father was inordinately proud of his

own commanding six feet of stature. From time to time he would measure me against the wall; and his few expressions of satisfaction in any performance of mine had almost always been in this physical growth, well above the average for my years.

Clearly he wished his Name to be represented by a tall man, like himself externally at least. And when this disease checked my growth, he took it as a personal affront.

For the next year or two he would measure me as before—and throw down the tape in disgust as the shameful fact became apparent.

It was more than a personal failure on my part; it was disobedience. He wished me to be tall. I did not comply. It must be that same secret lack of complete submission he had suspected before. That threatened the whole orderly structure of his cosmos.

Worst of all, he found himself at a loss to devise any new and subtle punishment which would eradicate this baffling defect.

All he could do was to increase his general severity. This he did, noticeably. With an added factor of deep resentment. Indeed, I think he began to dislike me actively from the hour when he accepted the bitter truth that I would never be any taller.

Nature is indefatigable and amazing in her efforts to build up resistance to anything which threatens a living organism.

You will see a weary old horse whose hide is so inured to cruel beatings that he does not even hasten his tired shuffle when the whip lashes his sides.

I think my mind and body went through that same toughening process.

Still, while a boy may learn to hunch up his shoulders and "take it," yet give no external sign, that personal animosity from the person closest to him produces an inevitable effect.

I went through the natural alternations of bewilderment, resentment at injustice, futile anger. There were times when the religious confirmation of the command for "unquestioning obedience" made me wonder if it were not myself who failed in some primary duty. But abusing myself, deciding I was wicked and abnormal, did not help.

After all, there was Cousin Peter for comparison. He was in my eyes everything a boy should be. Nobody made such requirements of him—and there were times when he expressed the most shocking criticism of my father's iron regimen. Moreover, I could not see that any other boys I knew were subject to such extreme rigors.

It was long a hopeless puzzle; but necessarily the opposing forces lined up more clearly each year: the Church precepts, completely backing my father, on one side; Peter, and most of the rest of my human world, on the other.

The exact theology of any church is difficult enough for an adolescent, if he once becomes vitally interested. Everything is easy so long as he accepts these strange authoritative statements as one more puzzle in a world he does not have to understand in order to live comfortably in it.

This "Why?" became an insistent everyday problem for me. I had to obey. There was no use of arguing or protesting. But in those secret, still unconquered recesses of my being I was compelled to attempt to reconcile these violent contradictions—the Captain and the Church on one side; all my instincts and observation on the other.

It may be that I am not "religious" anyhow. Certainly I found private questions and doubts more and more bitterly assailing the beliefs I was ordered to accept.

There was no one to whom I could confess even the fact of that unhappy conflict.

Naturally there was built up a completely hidden personality, unknown to all except my alertly suspicious father.

That odd, lonely little self finally discovered it did not, could not, believe some of the most vital doctrines of Holy Church. To be sure, I was far from having developed enough character or courage to do anything open about that. But there was the hidden Thing, ever growing and hardening within me. There was no cheer in it. Only black hopelessness.

Nor did it add to the cheerfulness of the situation to reflect that all the experts about me would have informed me I was surely headed for eternal damnation on this count alone.

CHAPTER IV

I Meet Love

TWO YEARS AFTER THAT TYPHOID FEVER produced such an unexpected embitterment of my already dreary relation with my father, I suddenly found myself in the grip of another youthful fever.

I was very unhappy. I must have been deeply ashamed of the unnatural subjection in which the General (he was that now) held me so relentlessly; and while I had not yet so much as visioned the possibility of breaking loose from this servile condition, there was a constant, hopeless inner conflict.

I grew more silent, more driven in on myself, more mechanical in my relations with an outer world which seemed to have little meaning, and that disagreeable.

Then my religious doubts grew like weeds. Those definite, exact formulations of doctrine, which any church demands of believers, have to be swallowed whole. Once broken up, analyzed, critically examined by a reasoning faculty, only a few can accept them as literal infallible truth.

I was not of that few.

I had been forced to question the validity of the religious sanction given by my church to my father's tyranny. Soon I found I simply did not believe one profession of faith after another which I had been automatically repeating day by day.

Far from feeling any pride in this, it distressed me deeply. I was nowhere near having developed enough mental or spiritual independence to imagine for an instant I could proclaim my scepticism, stand by myself. I had to submit once more to this alliance of Powers who were not content with ordering my whole outer life, but insisted also on dictating my deepest, most personal beliefs.

All that was individual in me resented this, resented the pretence and deception to which I was driven. I began to hate the seminary school, and everybody connected with it.

Then one day, another boy in a burst of generosity (or because he had tried them) gave me most of a capful of green apples. They must have been pilfered by night from a neighboring orchard —but I was quite in a mood to share the loot of others' crimes, especially as an innocent receiver.

I munched the unripe sour fruit, trying to believe it was delicious because it was such a break in our Spartan fare. Even the curious, expectant looks of the open-handed donor did not warn me.

I was rather run down anyhow. My mental disturbance had produced a physical depression which laid me open to any sort of ailment.

Naturally enough, a few hours later I was bundled off to the infirmary with a high temperature and a raging colic. The doctor took it as a matter of course that I would presently develop the German measles which was prevalent. Better isolate me a few days, just to make sure.

I lay on the narrow cot in the empty ward as darkness fell.

My head seemed to be a balloon, swelling and swelling until the enveloping fabric must surely burst. The violent pains had been purged away with equal violence; but I was exhausted and completely miserable. I seemed to be in a strange world. And nothing could be more hopeless than to find that any other world was even less pleasant than the one I had been in before.

Then I beheld an Angel.

She moved noiselessly toward me through the dusk, holding a lamp whose light fell upon her oval face, her great dark eyes that were so alive and yet so kind.

Her costume was that of the Sisters who acted as nurses in our hospital. But I knew at once she had walked right out of the altar painting in the Cathedral. For she seemed to embody all that mixture of earthly and heavenly adoration which the fervid early Christian artists expressed when they tried to picture the Virgin.

Also her motion was just that of one of Botticelli's goddesses advancing across meadows sewn with little spring flowers.

Happiness came with her—and I smiled for the first time in a long while.

Gently, she placed the lamp on the corner table, and bent over me.

I felt the exquisite soft coolness of her firm hand while it pressed my temples. I heard the inarticulate cooing sound of sympathy as she stroked my burning forehead—like the sound of a pigeon on her nest.

Almost at once, still smiling, I fell asleep.

At that moment she was not a real flesh-and-blood person. I am sure I never expected to see her again. But I was equally sure that I would see her forever. And there was more active pleasure and excitement in that thought than I had experienced in my entire sixteen years of living.

Next morning I woke to a basic physical sensation of emptiness.

Then this lovely vision appeared again. She was nursing me, making me comfortable, with feminine tenderness yet with the gaiety of her own young health and irrepressible high spirits.

The breakfast gruel for which my hungry stomach was calling seemed quite unimportant beside the craving to absorb her freshness and charm through my wondering eyes.

I always see the picture like that: she on the

verge of delightful laughter; and the solemn youngster in removed adoration, sharing her bubbling feeling merely as a part of her.

"Eat your breakfast," she commanded. "Haven't you as much sense as a blackbird? There are two of them in the tree out there, fighting over the ripe cherries. They were so savage about it I thought they'd pick each other to pieces."

I spooned up the watery mixture. Mandragora or henbane would have been delicious if she would only stay and keep on talking.

"A little temperature still," she announced presently. "But you go up and down like a thermometer."

Even in my mazed state I could have explained that—to myself. All my powers of secrecy would have anxiously concealed from her how the blood rushed to my temples as she came near.

My only conscious thought was a haunting apprehension that perhaps this blissful condition of nearness might not go on forever.

The digestive upset which had brought this magic was soon over. In two days I was quite well again. But for the only time I can recall I became a malingerer. I invented pains. I pretended sorenesses. I tried to create a rapid pulse and a high temperature.

My normal male feeling of shame at being "sick abed" was entirely submerged. If I could have gotten hold of another capful of green apples I would have tried blindly to repeat this prodigious experience. I wanted to be ill—anything to postpone the terrible moment which would take me away from such mute ecstasy.

I am certain the beautiful Sister, perhaps ten years older than I, saw through me from the beginning. Doubtless she was as compassionate toward my sudden emotional seizure as to my physical suffering. And looking back, nothing could have been finer and more womanly than the way she permitted me to adore her, without crushing my youthful passion by showing her maternal attitude.

Her own situation was strange, and hardly cheerful. Forbidden by her family to marry the man she loved, she had carried out her threat to "go into a convent" by joining the sisterhood as a novice.

But this I learned later. No one could have imagined that past unhappiness, or the exacting future ahead, while watching her eager human service, and especially the charming gaiety which continually broke through her professional reserve and her personal sadness.

For more than a week I managed to stave off the inevitable, developing a series of contradictory "symptoms" which would have bewildered an earnest attendant physician. Indeed I displayed an ingenuity which I can hardly pronounce "worthy of a better cause," but which was at least a tribute to the fervor of my concealed emotions.

I might have kept on indefinitely with these childishly transparent attempts at shamming. But one morning, as I related a piteous tale of a suffering, tossing night, I caught a gleam of humor in her great eyes.

That was enough. The one thing worse than leaving her was to betray my cherished secret, to have her laugh at my juvenile folly.

My recovery from that instant was so rapid that the very next day I was pronounced fit to go back to my classes.

The Sister's smile was full of tender comprehension. It was almost worth the pain of leaving to receive such an intimate personal message.

I suppose a boyish first love is about as ethereal and selfless an emotion as a man's life offers him. Extravagant, obsessing as it is, it demands nothing. It feeds on stolen glances. It will labor and contrive endlessly to achieve a casual meeting. It repeats instinctively the most excessive, prodigal, unreasoning acts of the romances of Chivalry.

For weeks afterward I would spend hours waiting at a distance outside, just to catch a faraway glimpse of this figure speeding from the convent to the infirmary. I could distinguish that quick bird-like motion as far as I could see.

Once or twice I managed to invent an errand plausible enough to take me to the hospital office—amply repaid when I once found myself actually speaking with my divinity. Then I left the distasteful seminary school forever.

Absurd as it sounds, I fancy that was as near as I ever came to being utterly in love with any woman. There were plenty of brief illusions in the next twenty years, but I recall nothing of such intensity or complete possessiveness.

I never knew what became of Sister Agnes. I hope she found the right man and made him as complete and happy as she was capable of doing. There was little in the rest of my life comparable to that idyllic interlude.

As for myself, I went to the officers' school, crossing at one step the line between boy's and man's estate.

Contrary to the usual experience, women came to mean less and less to me.

For a man has to forget himself to be really in love. And my training was calculated to drive me ever more inside myself, putting me always on guard, destroying any power of open, natural expression.

Everything worked together to make me what I became.

CHAPTER V

Rebellion

THE OFFICERS' COLLEGE, WHERE I NOW found myself, was a smoothly functioning demonstration that the Army is an exacting mistress.

I had always known a driving routine of hard study; but here was a training school which seemed to say: "So you think you're fit to become one of Us, do you? Very well. Just for a beginning you may acquire most of what men know in applied mathematics, chemistry and physics. Of course, too, you must be an engineer. You will learn languages and how to handle men. Naturally you must become an expert swordsman, pistol-shot, artilleryman and mechanic; and something of an athlete. After that we'll begin to test you."

And then the machine quietly sucked in the hundreds of young applicants and proceeded to see whether they could be manufactured into something useful, while this vision of the ultimate requirements was gradually unrolled before their eyes.

I was interested, even if a little awed, at the picture of what lay ahead. But of course, whatever it was, I had to take it. From my birth this was the thing for which I was destined.

Indeed the tradition was so ancient that my own life was merely a trifling incident. For thirty generations of my line, the oldest son had been born, not into the world but into the Army.

I could as soon have questioned the solid earth under my feet as this foreordainment—even if the reality had little relation to those triumphant charges of unscathed cavalry which had aroused my childish enthusiasm.

In point of fact, I was far too driven by the work to think often of anything further on. Daily report cards and periodic examinations produced enough imminent worries to ward off any more distant ones.

The riding and swordplay and shooting kept some sort of physical balance. And a final source of content was that Cousin Peter was also at the college. With him I could forget my loneliness. In presence of his cheerful high spirits my humiliating relation with my father seemed like a bad dream: it would surely return, but for the moment there was natural laughter, occasional sports and games, even a timid sharing in some of his reckless escapades.

It was a good life, compared to what I had known. Though I did not grow any taller I became stocky and exceptionally strong. At fencing and riding I could hold my own with almost anybody in my class. My forced concentration on study gave me high rank in the rigorous schoolwork.

So my crushed self-esteem began to revive like a trampled plant under rain. After all, I was not so hopelessly inferior. I could stand on my own feet among these picked young men, from all over the country, who had seemed at first so wonderful. Most surprising of all, they themselves recognized openly that in various matters I was superior.

That made a fellow's shoulders go back, turned his disturbing thoughts outward.

Inevitably, however, this very relief from my instilled sense of inferiority made my relation with the General increasingly unendurable. As the months lengthened into years, the joyful anticipation of holidays was quite overshadowed by the remembrance of what awaited me. I came to dread the black hour when I should again face that stultifying slavery; should see the haggard wraith my beautiful mother was becoming; should behold all about me the exaggerated, hypocritical religious observance into which she and my sisters retreated as the only protection against my father's waxing tyranny.

If I were really a man, as I felt myself, ought I not be the one to protect them against this household monster?

And again I would feel that inexorable régime engulf me—and would submit without a word.

I used to think about that; trying to understand. It was not that I was afraid of my father personally at this period. It was the fear of open conflict with my own flesh and blood, a sort of horror at defying this ruler who knew himself supreme, who would consider such conduct against nature, against law, against religion.

So I obeyed all these grotesque childish regulations. I never questioned an order. Like the others, I kept silence at table unless addressed—even when I was twenty and two of my sisters were grown women. I meekly came home from any evening party at ten. Externally, I was utterly subservient.

But a dictator must be sensitive to rebellion long before it breaks out. The General understood. He tried deliberately by increased severity to drive this hidden revolt into some open explosion where he could deal with it. And when my acquired endurance withstood all he could devise, his resentment grew to monomania.

It was during this period of bitter silent war between us that my inexperience of life plunged me into a scrape that for a time left me bound and helpless in his hands.

To begin with, I became momentarily involved in an affair of Peter's.

My cousin was a year ahead of me in age—and ten years ahead in freedom of action. I liked him immensely. He was my friend. He was almost the only person in my world with whom I felt intimately at ease. Naturally enough, I was carried along on some of his deviations from the rules, which were really quite normal for lively youth but filled my routine being with the thrill of breathless adventure.

We were on the way home from the college one time when Peter, fingering the sprouting mustache which now labelled him a man, confided to me he had a mistress.

"No!" I said, round-eyed.

"It's true. She's a charmer too."

There was a pause while I tried to adjust my mind to this prodigious development. So this lifelong companion was really setting out to explore those uncharted seas.

"Who—who is it, Peter?"

"A wonderful girl. I met her last Easter. She lives with her people, over in the south end of town. We have to meet secretly."

I looked at him in fascinated awe.

"Are you—are you going to see her this time?"

"Of course. This evening. I tell you that makes it exciting to come back."

"I suppose it does."

"That's what you should do, you old Sobersides. You're getting to be a regular stick-in-the-mud. What are you smiling at?"

"At the thought of what would happen in my home if I did do such a thing."

"Oh, well—I suppose the General would explode like a hand-grenade. But that's another thing you've got to tackle, the sooner the better."

"What do you mean?"

"You can't go on forever letting yourself be treated like a small boy."

"I'm glad to hear it."

"However, that'll come later. What I want now is for you to come with me to-night and meet my Theresa."

"Oh, my heavens! He wouldn't let me do that."

"You see? It's perfectly ridiculous. You mean to say you can't go out for the evening with me?"

"Yes. I suppose that would be permitted. But I'd have to be home at ten."

"Ten! Theresa can't steal away from home till ten. Just say you don't know when we'll get in."

I felt myself getting red, even with this trusted friend. "I couldn't get in at all on that basis."

"You mean to say you haven't—" Peter broke out.

"No. He's always refused to give me a latch-key."

"Well, I'll swear! That just shows you've got to do something. Still—the first thing is to get to-night fixed up. I'm determined to have you meet my girl."

"I don't see how—"

"You tell Uncle Charles I'm giving a little party and I want you there. Ask him to let you have a key for that one evening."

"He won't do it."

"I think he will. Anyhow, you can ask him, can't you?"

He never knew how much resolution was needed for my "Yes." It had become almost a point of honor with me to ask nothing of my opponent in this strange, unacknowledged duel. But I did want to take an outsider's part in this exciting business of my cousin's.

Peter's healthy, confident independence had the usual effect of making my own situation appear like a bad dream. This was the one intimacy my father had not only permitted but encouraged. Perhaps he would consent to relax his stringent regulation for this one evening, at Peter's special request.

And in the glow of my new resolution this began to seem probable, almost certain. I allowed my imagination to play on the coming novel experience. What would this "charmer" be like? As Peter's friend, how should I treat her? Suppose I myself should presently walk this romantic road along which Peter was adventuring! But imagination balked there. There were too many hurdles in the way.

Everything seemed favorable at first in my home reception. My college tests were good. There was a special note from the master-at-arms, noting my laudable proficiency with the sabre.

The General inspected the record and had no rebuke—which was high praise from him.

I screwed up my courage.

"Cousin Peter has asked me to go out with him this evening, sir."

"Where?"

"He did not say."

"Well, you can go. I do not approve of my brother's laxness in training, but at least his son is one of us."

With great effort I prevented my voice from trembling:

"Peter says he is not quite certain when we shall get in. May I have the front door key, so I need not disturb anyone?"

"The key? Certainly not. You will be home at ten as usual."

"But, sir, he has made some plans—"

"His plans have nothing to do with you. Do you suppose I shall permit a son of mine to wallow in this provincial town's night filth, for all these bourgeois yokels to gape at and snicker over? Ten o'clock, as usual."

"But, sir—"

"You have your orders."

I was silent. I knew protest was worse than useless: the least hint of it would probably bring a curt forbiddal of going out at all. But I went to my appointment in the fatalistic spirit of the man inexorably driven into a deadly sin, and hoping to store up something worth remembering against the hour of punishment.

Peter and I investigated the meagre night life of the town for some hours. At the appointed time, ten o'clock, we were at a table in a certain café.

After a wait, we ordered something to drink. Soon my cousin began to fidget over his lady's non-arrival. I calmed him. I myself was already an outlaw. I understood the strange equanimity shown by criminals who have definitely crossed the legal boundaries.

It was after eleven when Theresa appeared, breathlessly explaining the break in family routine which had prevented her from creeping out at the expected hour.

"At this moment I'm supposed to be fast asleep in my room," she giggled.

"If that supposition were true," I remarked, "there would be—two—very desolate young men loose in this town."

She laughed gaily. She was young and fresh and pretty, quite flattered at being picked out by a young officer of a higher social class.

It was with almost a sense of treachery that I realized she did not seem nearly as wonderful as I had gathered from Peter's description—and as he appeared to find her.

That made me more respectful and more flattering. We had food and a bottle of wine, and stimulated by her gaiety and the unspoken feeling of these two, we were soon laughing and talking in easy intimacy.

Our choice little supper was not over till long after midnight. It was another half hour before I felt I could leave them for their voyage to Cytherea, without being grossly obvious.

So at the unheard-of hour of quarter past one I found myself alone in the dark and deserted streets, automatically headed toward home.

On reluctant, leaden feet I advanced slowly through a world of gloomy night, which at each step became more strange and forbidding.

With no real hope I tried to imagine I might find some window left unfastened, through which I could crawl quietly, and find safety in my own small room without awaking my martinet father.

The knowledge that this would be a miracle operating for my special benefit did not tend to hasten my pace. I must have taken half an hour to cover the last quarter-mile.

It was no surprise to discover from stealthy exploration, all round the silent house, that there had been no helpful lapse of carefulness on the part of old Albert. Everything was securely locked. There remained nothing except to announce my own criminality by ringing the bell at the front door. Either that, or sleep on the ground somewhere outside the kitchen, hoping to steal upstairs when Albert came down in early morning.

That seemed too poor a chance. And to be caught in daylight would be even worse than whatever confronted me now.

Setting my teeth, I walked to the entrance.

Before I could ring, the door was thrown open. The General stood there in the hall before me. He was in uniform, his face that of the presiding judge at a summary court-martial.

He wasted no time in such trivialities as statements or pleadings from the lawbreaker. I am sure he was priding himself on his magnificent restraint.

Hardly was I inside when he pronounced grim sentence.

"You will pack early," he announced. "You return to the school on the first train. You will carry this order from me to the Commandant, placing you on bread and water in solitary confinement for two weeks."

No appeal even to be thought of. Rhadamanthus—Yahveh had spoken.

And so it was. The day after I had journeyed home for the week of relaxation I was headed back—to arrest and disgrace.

When Peter came the following week, he used all the new oaths he had picked up. He found more efficient consolation, however, in dwelling upon the expedition to the neighboring Casino which was planned by a crowd of us for some months later.

"For once you're going to see something of life," he declared. "Even the General can't stop that."

This class relaxation of discipline was a tradition of long standing. The group was to descend in a body on the gay Spa crowded with pleasure-seekers. Here we were supposed to make a first acquaintance with the gambling temptations each would meet constantly in later life. Anyone can imagine how it was looked forward to by young officers under this rigorous training for ten months out of the twelve.

In my own case the main problem was to get enough money in hand to carry out the object of the adventurous trip. For two years I had been penuriously saving my minute allowance with this in view. I had gone without necessary clothing, cut out all little luxuries, watched every expense like a miser, in order to amass a few hundred dollars and be able to keep step with my fellows on this momentous occasion.

It did look as if for once I might escape from surveillance.

My military punishment, and the small routine of college work, and the anxious crucial examinations were past at last.

I could hardly believe it when I woke one morning of sunlight and realized the great day, so long anticipated, had actually arrived. I was a sub-lieutenant now. This escape from grinding routine seemed to symbolize freer life just ahead.

Every incident of that eventful expedition etched itself lastingly on my memory.

The fresh wind in our faces as we surged out of the college gateway, and the liquid gold into which a blazing sun had turned the little river. The skylarking at the station and the ironical cheers as the fussy, little antique train puffed wearily in. How we took possession of the car, roughhousing and exercising our loud wit upon everything, regardless of the other passengers. The puzzled look on one old peasant's face as Peter and Joseph put on an act, involving some repartee with racy double-meanings—and his expression as he got the sly point and burst into a hee-haw, minutes after they had gone on to something else.

Then the smiling little city, with its holiday air.

We stared at the pretty women in smart frocks all the way from Paris, rolling by in shining carriages, while the sleek horses pranced and jingled curb-chains. We sampled half a dozen cafés, observing everything, and finding added excitement in the joint effort required to bring away safely two susceptible members of our group, who had succumbed to the obvious allure of a pair of professional sirens.

And at last the Casino itself, this ornate temple to the maddening goddess of chance. The regulars, with their controlled tense faces. Anxious losers. Feverish twitching winners. Perfumes, the white shoulders of women, the subtle undercurrents of sex. More powerful than all, the mass impact from the eager emotions of some hundreds of human beings, obsessed with the desire of money, the momentary possibility of winning thousands.

We were engulfed by this swift current and swept away.

With the special allowance for this Occasion added to my laborious accumulations over two years, I had in my pocket the equivalent of a thousand dollars. It was more money than I had ever before seen, much less controlled, at one time; the Count of Monte Cristo had no more intoxicating sense of boundless resources than I. It was not primarily the money, but the sheer excitement which drew me to the roulette table.

Characteristically, I separated from the other fellows. Working my way through the throng of players and watchers, I secured a standing-place close to this green table and the fateful red-and-black wheel on which focussed all eyes and all emotions.

It soon got me. That tense silence as the spinning wheel slowed. The explosive hissing breath when the ball rolled, bearing good luck to some, utter loss to others.

Silent and absorbed, I watched a couple of expert players, noted the results of their ventures, until I had grasped a few of the plays. A pallid Russian staked a hundred francs *en plein*. His number won. He looked almost bored as he took in the pile of money, thirty-five times what he had risked.

I was excited enough for two by this spectacle. That was the way I wanted to woo the goddess.

My birthday was the 19th. In the long years of my bitter struggle against my father's despotism this date had taken on an almost mystical significance: I felt that when I was twenty-one my condition must change of itself. And that liberation would come on the 19th day of a certain month.

Confidently I placed a hundred francs on 19.

The croupier chanted his monotonous adjuration—"Make your play, gentlemen." The wheel spun into a whirl of jumbled red and black. The professional warning sounded that the time for betting was past. The whirling circle moved slower, slower, slower—stopped.

19.

I was not even mildly surprised. I had known it would be so.

I will not detail the happenings of that feverish night. At one point I had almost ten times my original capital. At the finish I had lost not only my own thousand dollars but two thousand more —which I must pay before leaving the Casino, or be publicly disgraced.

I think that instant of coming to my senses from the gambling madness was one of the few moments in my life when I have been really terrified. It was waking into a nightmare.

In my panic all sorts of crazy notions beset my mind. Ever since I've felt I could understand any outbreak, however insane and grotesque, of a young man in such a predicament for the first time.

I am proud to say that I do not think anyone perceived my condition. Accustomed to think disagreeable things out by myself, I found a quiet corner, sat down, and looked the problem in the face.

Only one thing to do. Humiliating enough, even

with this trusted friend, but I must confess to Peter—and see what he could suggest.

I found him, gay with successful play and champagne, in the middle of the college crowd. Pulling him aside, I made a clean breast of my foolishness.

Peter burst out laughing.

"Why, you old son-of-a-gun! When you do break loose, you bust things wide open, don't you?"

"Looks like it."

"How much is it?"

Shamefacedly, I told him.

He pulled out of his pocket a fistful of bills, all crumpled into a ball. "Here," said he, picking out some big ones. "Get squared up. And take another whirl with the rest if you feel like it."

"Not I. I've had my lesson, for to-night anyway. I don't know just what I'd have done without you, Peter. I'll have to see what I can manage about returning this."

"Oh, forget it. Come on and have some champagne."

Naturally, it wasn't precisely the sort of thing

one can forget. And even the heady wine could not obscure the ordeal I saw ahead.

The tragic feature for me was that I must apply to my father. Of course Peter must be paid—and, since there was no chance of my saving or earning that much in years, there was no recourse but the General.

I faced that. I realized I would rather head the most desperate forlorn hope in battle than compromise everything I had won in our long struggle, by outer acquiescence and inner isolation. But there it was. I sat down that very night and wrote him a straight statement of what had happened.

His reply was completely in character.

"I am sending you a draft for the two thousand dollars you have thrown away. You will *immediately* pay this over to your cousin, taking his receipt and forwarding this promptly to me.

"The slightest reflection will show you that you have merely transferred your creditor. You now owe this two thousand dollars to me instead of to Peter.

"It is a large amount of money, especially for a

young man who has *nothing* except the allowance made him by a generous but just father.

"There is but one possible way in which you can discharge this debt within the next ten years; and, recklessly dishonorable as you have shown yourself in this disgraceful episode, no son of mine could possibly hesitate under such circumstances to redeem this small fragment of honor.

"You will write me at once your solemn, sworn obligation never again to touch cards, or bet on games of chance, as long as you live.

"For I have decided that, with this safeguard of my name for the future, I shall cancel your debt to me of this two thousand dollars."

I have known some bad moments in the half a century of which I have clear recollection. I have had my full share of danger, suffering and humiliation. But I honestly believe there was no other moment so bitter as when I read that letter.

In my abasement, the promise to abstain from cards or betting seemed a small price to pay for a clean slate. I swore as ordered. After keeping that oath for thirty-five years, I no longer have any desire for the relaxation of even the most innocent card games.

However, it was one more little outlet closed, one more push back into myself.

For a time my servile state at home was more complete than ever. There seemed no chance whatever that it could change.

But a man who watches other people's lives is continually confronted by a certain "morality of Nature."

Human acts which are violently "wrong," which do not conform to an equitable balance (often impossible to define at law, but instinctively recognized by normal natures), contain within themselves some principle which corrects them sooner or later. A devout Christian, or Moslem, calls this the act of God. The name makes little difference. One beholds the fact in daily life and throughout history.

I am convinced now that it was the very completeness of the General's triumph which led to the breaking of my bonds.

Perhaps it was his cold satisfaction over my helplessness, the ruthless way in which he took advantage of it, that destroyed some final instinct toward the reverence and affection a young man wishes to feel for his own flesh and blood.

Whatever the cause, the event came suddenly, without premeditation, as if it had been predestined—and the appointed moment had simply arrived at last.

Ironically enough, it came over a question of religious observance.

The General had grown more and more exact, and exacting, each year in his church formalism. He knew the authority of Holy Church to be his firmest ally in the absolute rule which had become the breath of life to him. He required more of us in attendance and strict conformity than the priest himself. One of the things I resented most deeply was the fanatical bigotry shown by an older sister, who had found this the one way to win approval from our tyrant.

On this occasion I had come home for a short vacation. The General issued his orders. We were all to attend a church service.

Then I heard myself (to my subsequent amazement) announce quietly that I was not going.

"What is that you said?"

"I'm sorry, sir. I find I no longer believe. It would be sheer hypocrisy for me to take part in a communion in which I no longer have faith."

"I did not expect such blasphemous and callow irreverence even from you. You will forget your sophomoric conceit, and attend as usual."

"I cannot do it, sir."

"I command you to do it."

"It is impossible. Those who feel that way should go. Until I change, I must stay away."

It was the first time an order of his had ever been so much as questioned in our household.

He was astonished, indignant, volcanic. He stormed and raved. He brought forward all his supporting heavy artillery: the dictates of God, Holy Church and himself. Threats of disinheriting and of hell burst about my ears like shrapnel. Threats of physical chastisement pointed their black muzzles at me.

Thanks to my long training, I remained calm.

Almost out of his senses with rage, he had caught up the heavy riding-crop which had for so long emphasized his disapproval.

Suddenly I found myself looking full into his enraged, bloodshot eyes. It was as definitely a duel as if we held rapiers.

"I am a man now," I said.

The uplifted cane dropped. For an instant I feared he was about to have a stroke of apoplexy. Then he turned away.

Never again did we come to such a personal crisis. But I knew from then on that he hated me —hated with that blazing, destroying wrath of the old tribal god toward the blasphemer who, by daring to question, actually weakens his divinity.

I wonder what happens to a man like the General when he dies, and goes wherever such men do go, and is compelled (as I am sure must happen) to contemplate the thing he made of his own life on earth?

More, to look squarely at what he did to the lives of those in his power?

What futile and childish inventions are blazing

hells and devils with pitchforks, and even the subtleties of Dante's seven-tiered Inferno, beside that inescapable self-judgment!

However, all that is someone else's responsibility.

After my assertion of independence I had the responsibilities of freedom, insofar as a soldier is ever free. Openly there was little change. My inner decisions were still secret, but at least there was no longer an attempt to dominate them.

I went back into the machinery which was to turn me out a soldier. Heaven knows, that discipline was stern enough. Yet from that day it was not unduly burdensome.

I began to look forward with interest and hope to the army career which was now so close ahead.

I knew, however, that in some respects I would always be different from the other men about me.

All this unnatural home repression, driving my instinctive reactions back within, to consider and feed upon themselves; all the constant necessity of concealing everything I really felt; all that effect was a chance product of being sired by a fanatical martinent.

Yet it did something irrevocable to me.

Always would my secret life be mine alone. The outer layer of "me" could and did take part in all sorts of social activities—and never betray that there was anything different underneath.

I was secret long before I was a Secret Agent.

And since there is always a place where an unusual human quality can be put to work in the colossal intricate human machine, it was only a few years later that this complex organism stretched out a cunning hand, laid hold of me as a cog in its unseen mechanism, and deliberately set about perfecting the involuntary training first begun by my involuntary choice of a father.

Indeed, from my later knowledge, I am quite sure that this particular human machine which claimed me had made preliminary studies of my character from my school days.

That Service begins early and spares no pains in investigating the material it may decide to use years later.

CHAPTER VI

The Army

No matter how carefully a man's future is planned, by others or by himself, life has a way of stepping in occasionally and twisting the pattern into a design quite unforeseen. Such a change comes occasionally as the sequence of some dramatic, explosive event; at other times it occurs quietly, matter-of-factly—like something inevitable which had been woven by the Norns into their inexorable tapestry long before.

I suppose it is that final unpredictability which keeps life so interesting. More even than dogged courage, I think, it is this perception of the infinite possibilities of to-morrow which would make suicide out of the question for a healthy man, even in his blackest hour.

A weak nature, beset for instance by crushing financial troubles, seeks for this imaginative help by focussing on a rich uncle who may die and leave a fat legacy; or a sweepstakes ticket that may come out among the winners. Some men of character succeed, while getting satisfaction from doing a job, in returning to a fundamental childlike confidence: the future may at any moment bring a quite unexpected turn for the better—and meanwhile they are confident they can meet whatever comes.

The acquisition of that mixture of belief in life, and readiness for its worst, marks a huge step forward in the art of living.

I was far enough from having developed such a reasoned and mature philosophy when, at the age of twenty, I received my official commission as a second lieutenant in the army of my country.

Yet during those periods of solitary reflection which had become second nature, I did perceive some larger, almost universal, significance behind the small events of my own unimportant history. It was almost like having a glimpse of that profound, inescapable "morality of Nature," of which a realist, philosophic friend likes to adduce examples from the lives of the most dramatic personalities of world history.

Here I was, after fifteen years' Spartan training, at the first definite mile-post of a career planned for me even before I was born.

From the very beginning I had accepted my father's grinding domination as one more grim fact in this cut-and-dried existence, where my own volition had so little part.

Gradually there had been built up the vague idea that "when I became a man" this crushing serfdom would change automatically. That must mean when I was twenty-one. I had made no definite picture of this, no preparation, no resolve as to accomplishing such an escape.

Then, by one stupidly reckless act, I had played right into the autocrat's hands, and had reached a depth of humiliation beyond anything I had experienced or imagined.

And, lo and behold! The direct consequence of this callow error had been my calm assertion of independence, and freedom without any struggle.

Thinking it over, I felt I should never again be really afraid of anything.

That sense of self-reliant power was strong within me as I packed my new uniforms into my new luggage, and prepared for the journey to the colony where the youthful officers of our army traditionally got their first taste of actual service.

The long trip overland and the sea voyage were not monotonous or tiresome. I had my established place in this great organization, won by my own efforts. A new world was opening up. It would be interesting to see what I could make of the opportunities lying ahead.

Above all I was breathing the air of personal freedom. The rigidities of army discipline did not trouble me, now that this black incubus was removed. Nor that automatic withdrawal of personality that had become habitual—which meant that I must live alone, finding most of my satisfactions within.

No. It was all so much better than what I had known, that my morale was high when I reported to the Adjutant at the colonial post where I was to be stationed.

The strange natives and new sights and smells were stimulating. I woke next morning full of curiosity and enthusiasm.

There was a shock awaiting me.

The first order I received was to report to the Colonel himself.

He proved to be a stocky, grizzled veteran, evidently a fine soldier and a man of the world.

Though he greeted me cordially, welcoming me into his official family, I was conscious of an exceptionally keen appraisal in his shrewd eyes.

"Sit down, Lieutenant. I want to talk with you."

I obeyed, wondering. I had been on trial before the General too many times not to recognize the court-room atmosphere.

"I believe in straight talk. For the moment I am not your superior officer. We are two men. You understand?"

"Yes, sir."

"Out here it is different from at home. When I send out a detachment I am responsible for its safety. I have to know the men I work with. Beforehand. You see that."

"Yes, sir."

"What does this mean? Straight, remember. Between two men."

He handed me a letter. There was an instant when my heart stopped short, as I recognized the General's writing. What now?

I read it slowly. There were first polite phrases. The General was a master of the dressy manner when it was called for. Then—

"My son, a lieutenant fresh from the college, will join your regiment shortly.

"Naturally, you need no suggestions from me as to the handling of young officers. But I feel it my duty, from twenty years of the closest supervision of the young man, to lay before you the conclusions at which I have arrived.

"He needs the strictest, old-time discipline, both on duty and off.

"Because I put the honor of the Army and of my name above any mere personal feelings, I say to you it is a case demanding close and unremitting control.

"For he is a boy who will disgrace his regiment, his family and himself, unless you drive him with a curb bit and a tight rein—as I have done all his life."

I looked up from the sheet of thin paper and met the Colonel's hawk-like stare.

"Eh? What the devil? What is all this about?"

"The General has always felt it necessary to arrange and supervise my every act. Even my thoughts. He could not bear that I should have an independent existence in any respect."

"Ah, I see. One of that old breed which confuse themselves with God. I remember now I have heard stories which I thought must be exaggerated. How long has this been going on?"

"All my life, sir."

"Yes. And now?"

"Of course that could not last forever. Last year—it ended."

"Hmph. And he cannot adjust himself to the present."

"Apparently not."

"I see. I see clearly. Listen, Lieutenant."

"Yes, sir."

"While you are with me I wish you to live a normal life. Nothing more. Nothing less. It will not be gay, out here; but after twenty years of—*that*—it may be good for you. Can you do that?"

"It will be heaven after the life I have had to live, my Colonel."

"Very good. Remember. Dismissed."

There was inner evidence that I had truly reached man's estate as I walked away from that surprising interview. For I had been swept by a natural surge of bitterness against my father, at seeing this cruel and unfair attempt to retain some fragment of control over me, even by this underhand method.

Yet this acrid emotion was quite submerged by my gratitude and my admiration for the Colonel's magnificent humanity.

I felt I could gladly follow that man against a battery firing point-blank. My mind was in a youthful blaze of determination to justify his confidence, to win a smile of approval by devotion to my soldier's job.

It was just as well that I had this extra personal incentive to carry me over the next year or two.

As the Colonel had warned, it was not exactly a gay life.

The novelty soon wore off, revealing a narrow treadmill routine which any intelligent man could master in a few weeks.

After that an ambitious young officer could try to pick up some words of the language; or he could listen to the veterans as they narrated bits of unwritten local history in which they had played lively parts; or he could retire to his own sweltering quarters and lose himself in the theory of tactics, dreaming of the superb counter-stroke with which he would some day demolish a superior force, by suddenly turning defense into attack.

And, just when it began to seem that this monotonous, directionless existence could never change, there came one of those quirks of chance which no informed imagination would have dared to predict as among the possibilities.

A little war sprang up, thousands of miles away.

That promptly focussed the attention of military men the world over. Peace had rested undisturbed upon Europe since some years before I was born; the idealists were beginning to demonstrate in print why there would never be any more wars: weapons were becoming too deadly, the bonds of international trade and finance were too close, the human animal was at last becoming too sensible, too civilized.

Men who have spent their utmost capacity in mastering the military sciences naturally do not feel that way. Moreover, even a little war piles up actual facts, that demolish old theories and serve as foundations on which to build new ones.

This was a minor war. But the "little fellow" involved was too pig-headed to recognize that by all the rules he was licked from the start; he took himself so seriously, and fought so stubbornly, that everybody else soon had to take him seriously.

Now, of course, it was not our war. We were

definitely professional spectators, watching two combatants work out with real men and guns some absorbing problems of modern strategy, tactics, assault and siege. We had studied these on paper: here was the living thing itself. Beyond this we could have no possible part in the conflict.

It was most surprising, therefore, to be summoned to the Colonel's quarters for another personal and private conference.

"Ah, Lieutenant. Once more I wish to speak to you man-to-man. And in confidence, eh?"

"Understood, sir."

"An odd thing has happened. Those people down there are born fighters, but they know nothing of making war. Now, by a queer chance, one of their improvised generals is an old friend of mine. Many years ago, before you were born, we were at college together. He has sent me word that their most pressing need is for a man on their General Staff who knows something."

"I can see that, sir."

"Yes, a few lickings have given them the idea

there might possibly be something in this skull-work after all."

"It's surely a chance for science to demonstrate."

"Perhaps. Anyhow, the idea has tickled my vanity, or my sense of humor, or something. I'm going. Quite unofficially, of course. Foreign expert volunteer. The Department knows nothing of it. Merely a leave of absence."

"Of course, sir."

"I shall need some staff officers. Volunteers, naturally."

"Yes, sir."

"If you should also find yourself with an indefinite leave of absence—"

"Yes."

"Would the idea of seeing some front-line work appeal to you?"

I was young, and there had been few whole-hearted enthusiasms in my life. I looked at this confident, capable human leader.

"My Colonel, if you told me you were planning to storm that seventh hell of Dante's, I should be honored to be invited to follow you."

He laughed, well pleased at my outburst.

"We'll work up to that gradually. Meanwhile, I have an idea we'll find it hot enough down yonder."

Every officer in the regiment jumped at the chance for such a "leave of absence." The Colonel was that sort of man.

So presently this rather incredible expedition actually set forth.

We finally arrived at a headquarters of chaotic disorganization—to find those obstinate individualists frankly contemptuous of our book-learning and scientific theory.

They were quite willing to have us organize a Foreign Legion, some twelve hundred strong, and if we chose to act under rigid discipline, that was our affair. (I may say our discipline was not so hidebound as to prevent us from smashing into a freight car, and helping ourselves to much-needed flour and tinned beef when the commissariat department failed us!) But most of them thought our hard-and-fast rules of tactics mere nonsense.

Even when one of their best leaders was captured with his whole force—from disregarding the Colonel's technical counsel—they considered it an act of God instead of an ignorant blunder.

We saw some hard fighting, and I for one learned a lot about actual warfare during that succeeding year. Also my admiration grew each week for our leader's knowledge, resourcefulness and fine humanity. But we were never able to function up to ten per cent in the department where we could have done them most good.

Even after all these years, I do not like to recall the climax of that interlude.

Our mounted legion was making a cross-country dash to reach a front-line spot where we were urgently needed. A native guide was leading us by a short-cut across the wild jumble of hills and rocks.

We trotted briskly down a rough track along the mountain ravine leading into open country. We were supposed to be nearing our destination, and were in high spirits at the cavalry feat we had accomplished.

Then we swept around a shoulder of rock—right

into the teeth of a strong enemy battery! The guide had sold us like a flock of sheep: they were ready, and waiting for our appearance.

A deadly blast of steel swept us head-on as the guns opened into us point-blank.

I saw the Colonel ahead go down amid a whole ghastly mass of stricken men and horses.

He never moved again.

Presently I knew that I was miraculously untouched, and that I and all who were left of our battalion were prisoners of war.

It did not seem to make the slightest difference.

This too was the Army. What had happened was a mere incident of battle, probably unmentioned in the newspaper dispatches.

It showed very little relation to those triumphant charges of lead cavalry which had so stimulated the martial ambitions of a boy of five, far back there in that former life.

There was not even that bitter satisfaction of hating the "enemy" responsible for this fatality.

For I must record that one of their generals saw

to it that the Colonel had fitting burial, and out of his own pocket paid for an enduring monument.

In that faraway land this red stone shaft still stands in the harsh sunlight, in memory of a gallant gentleman.

CHAPTER VII

A Service That Needs and Breeds Solitaries

We were herded into the misery of a prison camp, well calculated to drive any resolute man into an obsession of escaping.

With a few comrades I soon made the attempt. We got free, but were speedily recaptured, and returned to far stricter confinement.

Then I knew the sensations of being formally condemned to death—a punishment definitely within military regulations for such cases; of waiting day after day to be led out before a firing squad; and, suddenly, of being notified that the "enemy" commander-in-chief had countermanded this order of a stern subordinate.

All those alternations of emotion passed like some bad dream; but the daily nightmare of our condition was still insistent for action.

I finally won clear by an old soldier's trick. A plug of tobacco, steeped overnight in water, produces a nauseous mess which causes convulsive disturbance when taken into a human stomach. The effects simulate the first symptoms of the dreaded enteric fever, which was beginning to work havoc among us prisoners.

When the army medicos had certified my case, the authorities were glad to be rid of me. I left that place of despair, supposedly to die, in reality to return to my own army service in another colony.

After those tense days of scouting into the unknown, and the sudden bursts of guerilla campaigning, it was a terrific let-down to feel the confined routine of garrison duty close down upon my daily life and thought.

The differences between one post, one country, and another were all on the surface. The more that changed, the more it was the same.

Days merged insensibly into weeks, months, years.

For in the piping times of peace that closely planned army life is like an endless ocean voyage. The most trivial unexpected happenings assume vital importance—because they offer the only proof that Time is really moving and has not settled down to eternal drowsing in a placid Saragossa Sea.

A man does not even have any ultimate decisions to make, obligations to assume and worry over: all initiative, all responsibility is for those higher up.

A lieutenant must not think: he obeys orders. A captain (as I became in due course) thinks only when there is no Major or Colonel in the immediate background.

My first Colonel, now resting calmly thousands of miles away, had saved me from the worst effects of my father's attempt to reestablish his remote control by subterranean influences; but this baffled autocrat could at least flatter himself that, through the solemn oath he had exacted, he had deprived me of one of a bored man's chief resources—even the most harmless forms of card playing.

Now cards, and chess, and dominoes, and such "time-wasting" little diversions are life-savers to a man engaged in a mechanical routine, in a profession to which he was predestined by lack of any other taste and by the example of long generations of ancestors—but in which advancement during peace times usually means waiting for a superior officer to die.

During thousands of years men have learned the value of these trivial games in banishing vagrant unemployed thought. Thoughts will spring to life in the brain. And if not harnessed to some significant action, they turn carnivorous and rend their "master."

Every human being demands some lively interest. Excitement becomes in time as imperious a necessity as food and sex. Deprived of it, few men can remain healthily normal.

If this uplift, this temporary forgetfulness of self and small irritations, does not come from absorption in one's work and the illusion of that work's importance—it must be had from play. Else there begins a distortion of a man's whole outlook.

Some lucky men require only a charming woman in the offing to secure all the excitement they need.

There were charming women who appeared in

my restricted orbit from time to time. More than once, in a momentary blaze of sentiment, I fancied such a fascinating creature was truly the other self whom every man dreams of finding; but in no case did the illusion last long enough to land me in that bittersweet turmoil which is the supreme joy and torment of hot, questing youth.

I see now that no man could really love a woman while his deepest inner nature was focussed upon the self imprisoned within by such training as mine. Love is necessarily giving, giving all one has and is—because that has become the keenest desire, the most insistent demand of aroused feeling.

How can a human being give himself while he is watchfully aware of that self? When his first instinct has become to conceal any emotion, to suppress any impulse?

So in my stagnation there was no recourse in lovely women.

The ancient anodyne of drunkenness had small appeal for me—despite the whimsical justifications of a scholarly comrade, who pointed out how in various ancient civilizations getting drunk was a sacred rite: the god of the early Hindu, as of the Bacchic Greek, spoke through the lips of the intoxicated man. Not to mention, he would add, the self-evident fact that good old cognac was its own complete justification.

In a scientific spirit I investigated. It was not for me. Like any evolved gastronomer, I considered a real dinner impossible without wine. But a little satisfied me. And some native temperate quality made it impossible for me to find release in those relaxing potencies of alcohol. I suppose even there I could not let go completely. Anyhow, it seemed messy and stupid. I liked to keep my hands on the reins, to be in full control.

Cards, as I have said, were out completely.

I had not even the recourse of an intimate friend for argument and laughter and confidence. That same fixed glance inward, that self-conscious uncertainty with other unknown personalities, prevented my making any real friends.

There was little back at home to hold my fancy.

On my infrequent returns it was pleasant to see

Peter, who was advancing rapidly and would clearly be somebody in the Department. But my mother was gone. My father was embittered and almost querulous. My oldest sister was a bigot, horrified at my abandoned free-thinking. That atmosphere was even less stimulating than the cut-and-dried life of the post.

These wholesale excisions of normal preoccupations left little except my work, my ambition to rise in my profession, and books.

Hardly a balanced mental and emotional diet for a healthy, vigorous young man. Yet I lived on it. Perhaps it made for toughness of character. Certainly not for ease or light-heartedness.

And, as any psychologist could have predicted, those unsocial inhibitions increased all the time.

Once more I could see nothing ahead that aroused any eager anticipation.

Then one day, out of the blue, I was ordered to report to Q 2. That was somewhat startling.

For Q 2 was our Secret Service—so secret that a man in any other branch didn't talk about it. To be summoned there might mean anything: if one happened to have a bad conscience, it might mean running away as far and fast as possible—while knowing desperately that wouldn't be fast enough.

For the head of that Service had no superior except the Minister of War; he ranked as a Major-General, with peculiar responsibilities, privileges and summary powers. Should swift secret action be necessary "for the good of the State," he did not report or consult—he acted. And those people had their own arbitrary definitions of traitors. Also they were ever ready to justify their classification by sharp deeds. A man who let out national secrets in unfriendly company, however innocently, came easily within that definition.

Nothing of that sort troubled me. I had no women in my life to whom one must at times tell forbidden matters. The one whole-hearted allegiance of my existence was the Army, and the Government behind it which symbolized my native land. It would have been impossible for me to be indiscreet, even had I known anything to be indiscreet about.

Still, it was with lively curiosity, and with something more nearly approaching excitement than I often experienced, that I set out for the designated quarters.

Naturally, I had no thought except to obey orders precisely. That Army is the envy and wonder of the world for the intimate friendly relation which is a tradition between officers and privates; they meet on a common basis of race and broad human feeling.

Yet nowhere is essential discipline more rigorous, nowhere the judgment upon infractions of regulations more Rhadamanthine. It was that fixed precedent of course which made it possible for an egocentric, sadistic tyrant like my father to establish so crushing a despotism over his military family.

The Major before whom I found myself, in a retired little whitewashed cubicle, received me with the smiling intimacy of an old friend of the family.

"You are comfortable in your new quarters? And it is something to be a captain instead of a second lieutenant, no?"

"Yes, sir, it is a step."

"And it stirs your ambitions?"

"They do not need stirring, my Major."

"You wish then so ardently to rise in your profession?"

"It is all I have, sir."

"How is that? One has love, one gambles, one savors the good wine, one has a family, and friends."

"The Army is all that to me, sir. I have nothing, except the tradition of a thousand years to be a soldier."

"Then why—?"

And to my amazed discomfiture he began at the very beginning, nearly five years before, and recited, with all the proper emphasis, every single peccadillo, every least infraction of regulations of which I had ever been guilty.

It was like having the Recording Angel receive you hospitably, and suddenly pull forth your complete dossier and read inexorably through the list of things done which ought not to have been done—to say nothing of the things not done which a bit of initiative would have accomplished!

I am convinced that tall man facing me knew

even the fugitive, hot, impulsive, rebellious thoughts smothered without turning into acts, that I myself had utterly forgotten. I felt as exposed and naked as a bear in an open cage amid a crowd in the Zoological gardens.

I was scarlet, tongue-tied, in a daze. So this was the secret of my summons. What was going to happen? The cumulative effect of these petty misdeeds piled on top of each other was overwhelming. It must be like that to stand in the dock and have some relentless prosecuting attorney charge you with one crime after another throughout long years, till you realize you are a murderous apache, only fit to be executed.

Would I presently hear this calm emotionless voice announce that I was reduced to my former rank? Or could it be that I would be dishonorably dismissed from the Service?

I had a sudden devastating vision of my father's unholy joy at such fulfilment of his evil prophecies.

The Major's next words quite dumfounded me:

"We shall soon see if you have the makings of a Q 2 agent. You will be transferred immediately.

Report to the place mentioned in your orders."

"Yes, sir," I repeated mechanically.

"Remember always that now, in these dull times of peace, we may be only sixty in all, we who belong to Q 2. But when war comes, it is we who will have to handle the essential activities of thousands.

"And remember always that the first Law is *silence.*

"Carelessness with us is just as bad as treachery. Indeed, it is often more fatal: we can look out for traitors and open enemies; but a hundred wise men's efforts may be destroyed by one loose-tongued fool.

"There is a hard but true saying in the Bible: 'For it must be that offences come; but woe unto him by whom the offence cometh.'

"You may go."

I went out from there a very thoughtful young officer.

A week later I left the post and started on the long journey home—to enter my new and secret life's work.

CHAPTER VIII

Training

I had plenty of time for reflection during those weeks of travel. Back there when the century was young, one did not fly across a continent one day, and an ocean the next.

Just what was this mysterious work toward which I was heading, which demanded such searching selection and training of its agents?

My ideas of Q 2 and "Intelligence" in general were very hazy. Even as a child I had heard there were such things as secret services; but I had no clear conception of what they were for. I had read Fenimore Cooper's romantic tale, "The Spy"—which made some wartime features vivid, but certainly left a picture of a rather thankless profession; a boy reader preferred the independent scouting and fighting of Leatherstocking, matching his wits against the Indians of the forest.

Then at college I had learned of Herr Stieber,

whose advance organization of busy German agents at fixed posts in France had proved of such service to the Prussians during the War of 1870. And of that earlier Schulmeister, the Alsatian smuggler, who became invaluable to Bacler d'Albe in gathering enemy information, and was afterwards welcomed at court by the Emperor Napoleon.

But there seemed to be singularly few definite records in history of such activities, obviously necessary as they must be. The wandering Israelites did not dare to enter upon their Promised Land without sending spies ahead. Every army going to a strange country needs to get intimate facts of topography and peoples from natives or somebody. I could recall almost nothing giving a background of antiquity to this essential service.

There was an old professor of archaeology on the boat. He was so full of some sensational new discoveries in Crete that he was ready to overflow on anybody, and I listened for hours to his enthusiastic picture of that formerly unknown Minoan civilization, the rediscovery of which so profoundly altered our histories of classical antiquity.

"Do you suppose, Professor, King Minos had a spy system?"

"Spy system? Of course. Bound to. We haven't found it yet, but almost surely he had also one of those telltale whispering galleries, like that later Ear of Dionysius at Syracuse, where the Tyrant in his palace could go to a hole in the wall and overhear every murmur of his luckless prisoners in the subterranean cavern, two hundred feet long."

"You mean those things had to be, even back there."

"The pattern's always the same. As soon as a king, or an oligarchy, or a nation has supreme power, the autocrat begins to fear somebody will take that power away."

"So he has to find out the secret thoughts of all those others."

"Exactly. He's afraid of being attacked. Or he plans to attack someone. Haroun al-Raschid did his own spying in those nocturnal adventures of the Thousand Nights. And did you know that one day in Holy Week used to be called Spy Wednesday?"

"No."

"Because on that day the Sanhedrin sent a deputation to find out privately about this troublesome person, Jesus, and to trap him, by questioning, into some illegality. Then they bribed Judas to tell them where his Master would be that night. The details differ, but under the modern complexities it's always the same thing. Why are you interested in that?"

"I happened to be reading about Vidocq, during the French Revolution."

"Yes, he was a criminal, a police stool-pigeon, an *agent provocateur*. Then he became a famous man at his job. Evidently it's all necessary in the present stage of evolution of this queer human animal. Personally I'd rather find out something about Minos, and those amazing acrobatic priestesses of the Bull God."

He was off on his hobby again, and I listened abstractedly. My mind was little clearer on what lay ahead for my future. But I had learned to wait.

It seemed as if I had been travelling in a huge circle when I finally reported at the obscure town where the Q 2 training school had its unpublicized existence.

For this was only a hundred miles from my birthplace, though I had never heard a word of such an institution.

And when the C.O. curtly informed me I would be first assigned to the class in geography—three months of intensive concentration on geography!—I felt as if Time had actually turned backward, landing me once more in childhood's schoolroom.

I soon discovered, however, that this geography was different. A highly specialized form it proved to be—Military Geography.

I was confronted with a mass of encyclopaedic details about every capital and key city of Europe—not to mention a lot in Asia, Africa and the transatlantic world: its exact location, harbor if any, sea and land defenses of every sort; its railroads, highways, canals and water communications; those vital spots of the great modern metropolis—electric power houses and gas plants, water supply reservoirs, dams, bridges and tunnels, food storage warehouses—where a shrewd blow might cripple the giant organism.

Then the strengths and weaknesses of that whole country: its rivers, mountain passes and main roadways; the army posts and their garrisons, army and navy, systems of fortifications, munition and ordnance works, steel plants, oil supplies, mines, chief factories.

In short, this vast collection of statistics comprised an up-to-date gazetteer, containing practically every fact a man would need to plan an invasion of a given country, or the swift capture of a given city.

And all this kaleidoscopic jumble of precise information must be memorized exactly.

No notes. A man who could not write a line would hardly have felt the handicap in my branch of that Service: nothing must be put on paper which, in case of accident, could betray the operative or the organization behind him. Everything was to be patiently memorized, held in the subconcious, ready for instant use yet safe from the cleverest enemy.

As the magnitude of the task burst upon me the thing looked like a sheer impossibility. But other men must have accomplished it; and I knew myself to be capable of profound concentration. Anyhow, the first thing a man learns in the army is not to question orders.

I started in grimly. There was nothing to distract my mind. Through sheer repetition I learned the first batch of facts by rote. They meant nothing. The second city was mastered more easily. I soon perceived the amazing things hard practice and necessity can do in developing memory.

Presently these bare statistics began to take form: I got glimpses of the plans of these places, the topography was there before me, I was comparing the facts about one city with similar ones of another, grading them, spotting the joints in the natural and artificial armor.

That pitiless cramming went on for three months. I would wake up at night, to find myself repeating a catalogue of munition plants, or visualizing a diagram of railway arteries.

Then came the exhaustive examination about

which I had been so hopeless. And a miracle occurred.

I found myself completely at ease in this crucial test. There seemed to be in my brain an annotated map of the civilized world, as vivid and detailed as if Mars, God of War, looked down and beheld every past and present human activity in his honor.

A sectional rolled map, which at a question slid smoothly across the conscious stage of my mind, displaying every least fact needed for the answer. When my work in subsequent years took me to some of those cities for the first time, I discovered that I knew far more about them than most lifelong residents.

I passed that first test triumphantly. Had I failed I would have had no other chance. Those people had no time to waste on failures.

Complete as my absorption had been during those submerged weeks, many facts of this strange curriculum had forced themselves on my attention. When I could draw a long breath, I found I had a fairly accurate idea of the general outlines.

The aim of all the bee-like, often startling activities for which I was to be so solemnly trained was *To Obtain Information.* Military Intelligence is the official designation for the ever-ramifying duties of this most recently organized branch of a nation's military force. During the World War it was to grow into an organization of almost unbelievable complexity. Even in those years of calm its scope, and the relentless thoroughness of its methods, would have been a startling revelation to any outsider.

Information. For us that was the Chief End of Man, as your Catechism puts it. Information about every "enemy's" armaments, military condition, ships, fortresses, new inventions, plans, experiments, secret understandings. The greater the secret, the better the hunting.

And, of course, to our Service, as to any General Staff responsible for a nation's "preparedness," all other nations in the world must be theoretically potential enemies. To justify their existence the Staffs must have plans, filed away and ready to produce, complete down to the last legging button like those of the German strategists in 1870—for war with anybody.

Naturally, Generals cannot make knowing plans (any more than can a challenging prize fighter for the heavyweight championship) without knowing just what the other fellow has got, both in the way of attack and defense.

That was where we came in.

To secure a constant stream of up-to-the-minute "inside dope," on which to base these constantly revised plans for all conceivable and inconceivable emergencies, a marvellous technique and a body of binding traditions had been developed over a couple of centuries.

I perceived there were half a dozen chief sections of the training course designed to turn out competent workers in this exacting profession:

1. Special and technical knowledge of bewildering variety.

2. Razor-edge whetting of the worker's mind and body.

3. Mastery of the complex working tools of the profession.

4. The Science and Art of Securing Information.

5. Getting the Information back to Headquarters.

6. Offense and Defense in Emergencies.

There was plenty to learn in each of these divisions, even on top of the thorough training of military college, and five years' actual army service. That course had been worked out from bitter experience by keen minds responsible for the Service's cherished reputation of infallibility.

There were highly confidential textbooks. These had an ancestry dating back to the Thirty Years' War, when France and Germany—Catholic and Protestant, concentrated central authority and a shifting group of heterogeneous States—showed the world of what sub-human savageries homo sapiens is capable in the sacred name of Religion; also they dragged all the rest of us Europeans, actively or passively, into that terrible vortex of blood and tears.

These texts were revised up to the moment like a Wall Street broker's market and financial reports. They came in part from authors world famous in their own specialties; in part from men whose very names were unknown outside the Service, but whose first-hand knowledge was exhaustive, and whose enthusiasm for the cause was that of fanatical devotees.

Naturally, we used the pioneer work of French Bertillon on fingerprints, and some stuff on handwriting and physiognomy by great German scientists, as the basis for the expert manuals developed by our own technicians—just as they soon embodied in their works any new ideas we originated. Secret services cannot long protect their professional technique from other alert services.

The first sensation from all this was like that of being transported to the Catacombs, and realizing the rest of one's life was to be spent in this confusing subterranean labyrinth. Then bits of plan began to be apparent. And before long a man became so absorbed in mastering the plan that he no longer considered the darkness and concealment, or even the ultimate destination of his laborious wanderings.

I had come to consider myself well above the average in physical fitness and all-round capacity, as a result of my riding, fencing and campaigning; but the standards set by our instructors involved a prodigious amount of intensive physical training.

An agent was supposed to be a self-contained power-unit, ready to perform for himself any operation of everyday life, especially those of transport. He must be expert in driving a motorcar (or a plane, when those came along presently), running a launch, sailing a boat, riding any horse. It was required that he become an exceptional mountain climber, walker, skier, swimmer, diver.

His muscles were trained to instant explosive energy and to tirelessness; he must run till finding second wind became an expected commonplace; even gymnast's tricks—climbing ropes hand over hand, scaling walls, "human fly" feats—had to be included in the repertoire, since he could be quite sure of finding himself in situations where only the unexpected and extraordinary could bring him out again.

The spectacular feats of the New York firemen would have been child's play for our best agents.

The mental discipline went still further beyond the utmost one could imagine called for in ordinary walks of life.

We must be completely at home in at least four languages—and the more foreign tongues and dialects one could understand and imitate, the better the equipment. A man was expected to keep up to date in mechanics, applied physics and chemistry, new inventions, the shifting currents of politics and trade.

Memory and observation were cultivated to their extreme capacity. Everything must be carried in the head, to avoid telltale memoranda which might be lost or stolen. One must see everything at a glance. Then store it up, exactly as it was.

The parts of a face impossible to disguise must be studied so minutely that that face would never be forgotten.

Thus we learned that the base of the nose is full of individuality. That cannot be altered. Nor can the space between the eyes. Those identifications always remain like labels to the seeing eye.

There is unfailing revealment, too, in the way a man uses his hands, and all those other unconscious little habits of muscular expression. When you have noted it sharply, you can often pick out an individual as far as you can see him, merely by his way of walking.

All that grew fascinating. It was like the old unending battle between bigger and bigger naval guns, and thicker and tougher armor plate. On one side ingenious methods of disguise; pitted against those, shrewd observation of the minutiae which betray a given personality.

We learned all the stock tricks of make-up—false hair, changing the shape of nostrils, altering eye effects, and the rest. Also we learned the basic fact that these stagey aids should be dispensed with except on rare occasions; for usually the best disguise is sheer inconspicuousness. The ordinary eye and brain rarely gets more than a surface impression of a stranger—unless attention is attracted by something unusual.

There were courses in handwriting, frightfully complicated and difficult study of codes and cipher systems, methods of using and detecting invisible inks, sign messages, and so on.

Then much time was devoted to the tested methods of securing documents and information.

These involved a knowledge of locks—for at times drawers and safes must be burglarized. They involved also deep understanding of what might be called human locks. The most jealously guarded documents have to be in charge of some official; there are always subordinates familiar with the files. And it seems to be true that practically every custodian will succumb to some degree of personal pressure. If he can't be tricked or intimidated, he can perhaps be bought. If he is in debt, as most subordinate government officials are, he can surely be bought, by an agent who knows how.

So theft and bribery become recognized weapons in this stealthy battle to secure the secrets of other nations.

There were many more material implements of our trade whose use had to be mastered.

Photographs were invaluable records in a hundred ways, and we acquired expertness in the use of a camera under difficult conditions.

Our own specialty for making pictures surreptitiously was a concealed camera adapted (and we believed, improved) from the ingenious device worked out by Lumière for the French bureau. This hidden instrument had a magnificent Zeiss lens working at f. 3. The shutter was worked by a tube running to a bulb in the coat pocket. It was almost noiseless, and there were many occasions when it produced sharp photographs of people and scenes otherwise impossible to get. These tiny recording angels cost $300 apiece, and were well worth it.

The tools became more grimly suggestive as we took up the approved methods of removing awkward human obstacles which might stand between us and success in our missions.

An agent must be a crack shot with pistol or rifle, and understand all sorts of explosives. He must be a fencer, wrestler, jiu-jitsu expert, wielder of sandbag and leaded cane. There were those who from racial instinct added most skilful knife-throwing to this armory of attack; and we carried a large knife in the side pocket, the sharp blade opening by a spring: one sweeping motion brought it out, open, ready for stabbing or throwing. At short distances it is a most deadly weapon, with the supreme advantage of silence.

We knew the disabling stroke with the side of the open hand against the carotid artery or the windpipe, and the stunning or fatal blow at the base of the brain.

We knew the precise effect of the dumdum bullets from our little four-inch, .22 calibre, five-shot Bulldog automatic pistols: a tiny hole on entering, a six-inch cavity on the other side. Also the three spots at which to aim in close work—the jugular vein, the heart, just behind the ear.

Killing was not our job. It was to be avoided. But when the choice came between killing and discovery, as it surely would sooner or later, the killing must be cold-blooded, sure, instantaneous.

In accordance with this basic principle, there was

one final, culminating weapon for the most dangerous missions.

This was a tiny hypodermic syringe loaded with prussic acid. Most of us later added some other swift, deadly injection to this equipment. I knew one agent years after who specialized in curare, that obscure poison prepared by the Indians of the Upper Amazon; though the sale was strictly prohibited, he had journeyed six days up the river to Manaos, and through underground channels had paid about $25 apiece for several of the poison-impregnated thorns, each good for five deadly little pricks. His clinical observations were that there was almost instant partial paralysis, death followed in about ten minutes, and the body turned black.

When I became an active operative I acquired my own superior rarity—a West African hell-brew, said to be compounded from the venom of a small snake, and the virus of the tsetse fly. It was most highly recommended by a man who declared he had first-hand evidence of its potency, and I carried it for a decade—just in case.

These sensational weapons were not for show.

We were taught exactly when and how to use them. Later on we did use them. And they did their work.

But for the high patriotic motive informing us all, an outsider might easily have confounded portions of our curriculum with the school for training pickpockets run by one Fagin, and others with Special Courses in Murder conducted by a far more refined and ingenious Bill Sykes.

Running all through our training was the constant inculcation of Silence.

Silence about the most insignificant details. For some veriest trifle dropped by chance might fit into some other trifle picked up by a shrewd opponent—and that alert enemy might get a glimpse of a pattern which must at all costs be hidden.

Silence on everything, to everybody, in health or illness, at all times. Silence even in the face of that shameful death which was always lurking just ahead to entrap a careless worker.

On this prime necessity our trainers did not trust to admonition alone.

One of my fellow students in this strange post-graduate course was a young lieutenant, Heublin. He was clever, handsome, quick as a flash, a pleasure to watch in the athletic feats.

One free afternoon he was sitting alone in a little café not often frequented by our crowd. We worked under terrific pressure during that training year, and there were times when the desire to do something altogether different was almost irresistible.

A man walking past the table stumbled against a chair, and apologized in such genial fashion that the bored Heublin asked him to sit down.

The stranger proved to be a sociable and charming person. He was a keen, well-informed commercial traveller for a machinery firm, just back after a long business trip to America. His funny stories soon had Heublin laughing immoderately. After they had started on a second bottle, the Lieutenant found himself more cheerful and relaxed than for many weeks.

The traveller was interested in everything, politics, business, art, science,—especially in any home changes while he had been away. The Lieutenant felt flattered at having his statements and opinions received with such respect by so cosmopolitan a person.

"I met an interesting chap over there, a Scotchman," remarked the stranger. "He was working on the War Department in Washington, trying to sell the government something. I didn't envy him that job. My work's bad enough, but at least I can get a yes or no inside of six months."

"Yes, that must be a tedious sort of effort."

"Never know where you are. Get nine high muck-a-mucks convinced—and the tenth turns the whole thing down. Not for me."

"Nor me."

"He had a rather amusing story on those people, though. It seems an American inventor named Maxim found he couldn't do anything with his own government. So he went to England, became a British subject, and made a huge success of those same inventions, especially his machine-gun. He's just been knighted.

"Now, here's the point. This salesman is convinced the United States is going to adopt officially for their army the improved light machine-gun worked out by Sir Hiram Maxim, to whom they wouldn't listen years ago! That's one on the Yankees, isn't it?"

"It surely is."

"Sounded interesting, that new portable gun. This fellow says it's miles ahead of any other such weapon in the world. The Portable Hotchkiss can't touch it."

"Nonsense," declared Heublin.

"How's that?"

"All nonsense. He doesn't know what he's talking about. The Hotchkiss is superior in every way. I'll bet it won't be many years before they abandon those Maxims and take our model."

"Why, you talk as if you knew all about guns."

"I know about that. I ought to. It's part of my job."

The stranger burst out laughing. "Just my luck to spring a technical statement on a man who really knows. Anyhow, I'm glad to be corrected."

After some talk, he left. Heublin went back to

his quarters, with a vague sense of uneasiness which he could not explain.

The feeling was no longer vague next morning when he was summoned before a stern C.O.

"At five-thirty yesterday, Lieutenant, you entered into conversation with a stranger in a public café."

"Yes, sir."

"You had never met him before, had no idea who he was."

"He introduced himself as a commercial traveller."

"And you naively accepted his statement. And proceeded to discuss technical details of our army weapons. Also betraying to the dullest mind that you were in some position of confidence."

"I never thought—I am afraid so, sir."

"Do you really imagine, childish imbecile, that we will entrust the reputation of the Service to one who has no more control of his tongue than a gossiping woman?"

The Lieutenant was scarlet and quivering.

"In other times I have seen men stood up before

a firing squad for a smaller infraction of regulations. How do you suppose your superior can ever trust you again?"

"I don't know, sir."

"Nor I. I have drawn up the order for your dismissal from this Service—"

"Yes, sir."

"But I have not signed it—yet. Go back to your work, and see if you can prove that it should continue in suspense."

"I shall try."

"And in the name of all the Saints, put a padlock on your lips. Talk all you want, to anybody. But *silence* about everything connected with us or the Army behind us. You know nothing yet—but keep it inside your skull. Have you got that idea firmly nailed down?"

"Yes, sir."

"We shall see. Dismissed."

It was a shaken lieutenant who stumbled blindly back to his quarters, and whispered me the story.

"Your traveller was of course an *agent provocateur* sent merely to test you."

"What a fool, what a fool I was!" he groaned.

"Better learn to talk silently to yourself, as I have," I counselled.

It was not necessary to be a principal in one of those devastating interviews to put a neophyte on guard against the whole outside world. Reticence became a primary law of self-preservation.

Personally I could not imagine abandoning this wary vigilance even under the strongest feminine fascination—that traditional cause of self-betrayal. For under that ceaseless pressure everything important seemed to desert the surface and retire to dark depths of the mind: should even the lovely little feet of the most alluring woman stray in that direction, the sound would be an instant warning.

All that carefully hidden knowledge would creep silently away to a still more inaccessible retreat.

This iron restraint, on top of a year's training far more severe than that of a champion athlete, was designed to produce the exceptional human instruments required for that job.

When the time came for us to take active part in the work, we were ready.

Each confidential mission was to secure some information ordered by a superior officer. We might have no idea why it was wanted, or what it was to be used for. That made no slightest difference. Out we went and got it. No matter what the cost, in money or life.

The Service must never fail. It must never appear openly.

We were no longer men. We were numbers. Joined together, those numbers had a portentous significance. Alone, each was nothing. The individual's character, tastes, abilities, even life amounted to nothing, except as these could serve the purposes of Q 2.

Failure meant dropping out. Open disclosure meant disavowal by the Service—and whatever punishment was due an unttached spy.

That was the Tradition which held the loyalty of this remarkable group.

The time came when I took my place among the active gatherers of the secrets of others.

CHAPTER IX

A Workingman at Work

My first mission on my own was to secure drawings of a certain mechanism developed for the artillery of a foreign power. These guns were being produced at a huge ordnance plant in that country.

I imagined myself a mechanic out of a job, and proceeded to function in that character. I was dressed like any one of thousands of such workers. The Service machinery moved smoothly to land me in that town inconspicuously. The police could have searched me from the crown of my head to the soles of my shoes, and found nothing in the least suspicious. Facts and instructions were all hidden in my mind.

At once I began to operate by the formulas we had been taught. There was nothing to it. It proved to be a simple case of minor bribery. Everything went like clockwork, and in no time at all

I had delivered the desired tracing to the agency charged with transmitting it to headquarters.

I did flatter myself on one touch: I really believe the poor little draughtsman whom I used to get my drawing never quite realized he had been bribed, or that anything important had happened. That struck me as a piece of craftsmanship.

As I started home to report—again an indistinguishable laboring man with nothing incriminating on his person—I found myself admiring the shrewd technique in which we had been so carefully instructed. It was easy to see that situations would arise where an agent would have to improvise, where all his initiative and resourcefulness would be called upon. But for the great majority of cases the method had been reduced to an exact science—as in that rather unpleasant modern "art" of salesmanship.

Especially was it noticeable that the vast mass of human beings rarely "see" anything in the true sense, unless they are sharply interested. Put an accepted, commonplace label on a man or a thing, and most people never go any deeper. The surest way to hide is to be one of a crowd. Get inside some surface too ordinary to be noticed. Disguise should be an internal matter: the less there is of it outside, the better.

This same principle was particularly clear in a subsequent incident, where I came upon the operative of another nation at work.

The agents of that particular country have been so often depicted by romancers in just such circumstances that for fiction such a circumstance has been worn out—as some excellent words have become banal and shabby from overuse. Perhaps nature does imitate art.

Often I have seen eyebrows go up, and a politely cynical smile appear, when some member of a group of men made a statement which was a commonplace fact in the Service. Human vanity dreads being deceived by a tall story: it seeks protection in a surface attitude of general disbelief before anything unfamiliar.

However, this is what happened.

One of the great powers was launching a new warship.

Admiral Mahan's brilliant works on Sea Power in the '90's had focussed the world's attention on the naval arm and fighting ships; there had been furious building; and the Russo-Japanese war had provided the first actual demonstration for ninety years of what happened when these modern sea-monsters came to real fighting.

This latest cruiser embodied some new ideas and developments, and the international race was so keen that there was lively interest in the event.

Naturally enough, I was assigned to attend the festivities on this gala occasion, in a minor official capacity which made my invitation normal. The Captain was giving a large formal luncheon. All that was everyday stuff.

The lunch was excellent. Afterwards, with the freedom of the invited guest, I strolled about the decks of the new fighter, noting everything I could embody in my report—armament, engines, equipment, plan.

She was an impressive ship. There was plenty to see and ponder over as I wandered idly around among a host of seamen, busy at all sorts of tasks.

Undoubtedly she was going to influence the shifting emphasis on the types of warships to be developed in an effective modern navy.

Presently I found my glance returning to an inconspicuous little sailorman who was painting away at some retouching. Bent over, his hat pulled down against the sun's glare, he was absorbed in his mechanical job.

Nothing could be more casual, more routine. Yet there was something– My gaze kept going back to him. I moved across to one side where I could get a better view of his features.

Yes. No doubt about it. I had seen that face before.

And presently a trained memory brought the proper dossier from its unseen filing cabinet, scanty as it was.

Making an opportunity when no one was near, I came close.

"I know you," I said quietly.

He glanced up sideways with a quick little smile, shook his head, bent to his painting again.

"I know your face," I repeated.

Merely a shrug and another jerky shake of the head.

"This place is too public," I went on. "Come to my room at the hotel at ten to-night."

He gave no sign that he had so much as heard. But I left knowing he would be there. He too was a secret agent. He saw I did not mean to expose him: much better to meet in private whatever might threaten his assumed identity as an enlisted man in that navy.

He came. The circumstances gave me a certain power over him, and my duty was to use this "moral blackmail" to see if I could pry anything valuable out of him.

He had a good line of defense, that little fellow. He declined anything to smoke or drink, but sat down docilely–and merely listened politely to anything I had to say.

When my questions were easy, he would smile, and bob his head. When they were difficult, he would smile and apologize for his pretended lack of understanding.

At last I saw it was no use.

"All right. I see you don't mean to talk. It's not very important."

He was all wordless apology for my disappointment.

"I know you're Japanese. And I've seen you before."

"Very apt make mistakes about other peoples," said he, still smiling.

"You needn't tell me anything if you prefer not. I shall know all about you in twenty-four hours. Good night."

"A pleasure to meet," was his parting word, as he dodged out, clearly relieved in spite of his self-possession.

Of course our people had the facts about him. He was a captain in the Japanese Navy—incidentally outranking the commander of the great ship on which he was an insignificant seaman. Yet there he was, the least of the lowest, puttering away at his dull handyman jobs—but keeping eyes and ears open for every inside fact a shrewd brain and great professional knowledge could gather.

Why not? Japan and that country might be

good friends—yet one could never know what the future might bring. And the guiding minds of that navy, like those of any other, must know what even a friend considered the last word in guns and armor plate and speed and handling, in anything which might aid one's own designers and commanders.

I imagine there was no navy in the world during that period in which Japan did not have these keen observers, sending home first-hand reports.

All my preliminary schooling, acquired experience and inner resolution were needed for one enterprise that fell to my lot during those early years.

A Power had unostentatiously developed one of its harbors to a point which aroused the curiosity of all other Powers. Over a period of years it had poured out millions, and then more millions—on half a dozen impregnable fortresses, a great shipbuilding plant, immense docks, an interior canal, a grandiose embodiment of ardent naval dreams. A sure haven and indestructible base for a mighty war fleet.

Lately there had been still further improvements, which made our files of information sadly incomplete.

My modest assignment was to secure pictures and notes of the fortifications if possible. But above all I must penetrate the mystery of the great locks by which the fleet of new sea-hornets returned in safety to this secluded base after their ocean dashes.

These must be operated electrically. But how? And from what precise spot?

We had no data on those vital points.

Again the quiet mechanism deposited me within striking distance of my destination.

I was not a workman this time. I was a loafer, a dejected listless member of the unemployed. My greasy second-hand clothes and battered shoes had been purchased from a local slop-shop: that way one was more sure of blending into the general picture without any possible difference of cut or detail to attract attention. My own garments were deposited in a safe spot, to transform me again if, as and when I returned with my booty.

It was a depressing, raw winter afternoon. Leaden clouds lay in tiers across the sky. When the sun did pierce between those gray layers it gave a pale thin light which was almost worse than none at all. The northeast wind was chill and piercing. It was hard to walk slowly.

Under my listlessness I was keenly alert to every passing face; and when, in an almost empty block I saw a respectable well-dressed citizen cross the street to avoid meeting me, I felt sure my appearance produced the desired impression.

I slouched aimlessly along into squalid streets, gradually working my way toward the harbor.

None of the stolid folk I passed paid any attention to me. I was obviously one of them; I could contribute nothing except a tale of misery; and they had plenty of that already. Nevertheless, I looked in shop windows, made circuits, and drifted back on my course more than once, to make sure I was not being followed. When you match your wits against other professional men, you are dealing with the wiliest of all animals. In spite of the most perfect system and the utmost precaution, leaks do occur. And this thing was too important to take any chances.

Besides, while I should not have been there had I not been prepared to die in carrying out my duty, I had every intention of succeeding, and living.

Everything was normal. I was merely one more bit of human wreckage in a submerged world. Which was as it should be.

Aimlessly wandering, I reached the edge of the inhabited quarter. The sloping country beyond was covered with a thickety growth of birches, which in places came almost to the water's edge.

Dodging out of sight into this cover, I found several favorable points and spent quite a while in studying the harbor and the series of forts commanding it from every side.

Photographs were clearly out of the question. The best I could do was to note everything in my mind so minutely that I could at least draw a plan of the whole system.

Anyhow, it was those locks and their control in which we were chiefly interested. That unknown control chamber was the heart of the whole complex business. Merely to have its exact location would be invaluable. Nothing more fascinating to a military strategist than to be able to diagram in red such a vital centre; to know that one good "egg" planted *there* would instantly cripple the whole elaborate mechanism, make these prodigious locks useless, destroy at one blow the triumph of years of planning and millions of expenditure.

Patiently I watched from my concealment. Along the great retaining walls facing me armed guards kept watch. The entire stretch of beach opposite the structure was patrolled by sentries, each with a beat of fifty paces.

The lock itself was quiet. My closest scrutiny could detect no hint of the method or place of operation. My effort began to look childishly futile. Only the blindest chance could bring me what I was seeking.

However, we had many opportunities to observe how signally Chance favors the man who insists on sticking to the spot after reason has pronounced the case hopeless. I tried to forget that insistent, searching wind. I refused to visualize my ignominious return without the thing I had been sent to get. Doggedly I waited and watched.

Dusk fell. The northern darkness settled down. Anger possessed me against those silent, insensate walls which hid what I wanted, against guards, sentries, everything. Under the spur of this emotion I took a desperate chance.

Stealing down to the shore half way between two sentry-posts, I slipped into the icy water of the bay. Very quietly I inched my way through a bed of tall rushes. Then, with the numbing water almost up to my shoulders, I slowly worked out toward the lock.

The water got no deeper. In fact, half way out, I found myself standing on a slight shoal. On this vantage-point I stood still, and watched again.

The slow minutes were as monotonous as the lap of the little waves against the concrete walls. I thought of nothing—not even whether, if by some miracle I did get my facts, I would be too benumbed to move back and try to escape. All my mental powers were concentrated in a complete alertness, ready to seize the slightest hint of the secret I must pierce.

Hours passed. There is a second wind in suffering as well as in running. When a resolute mind refuses to admit the pain upon the lighted stage of consciousness, tortured nerves seem after a while to lose some of their capacity for transmitting feeling.

Deep night had settled down upon land and harbor and sea far outside. No moon, no stars. I had figured on that. No sound, except the measured tramp of the sentries, the provoked *slap-slap* of the waves against this man-made obstruction.

It got to be long past midnight. That meant I had but three or four more hours before even the sullenest dawn would expose me. If any favoring quirk of chance were to aid, it must come soon. Impossible to imagine what form this hypothetical piece of luck might take. Concentrate your whole being into the keenest attention of every sense. Refuse admittance to the whining protests of half-frozen muscles and blood.

Wait.

At last. A noise. Something actually about to happen in this unending, hopeless misery.

Something! A gift straight from the goddess of luck. A vessel, coming into the lock. One of the veritable sea-hornets, returning by the canal from a cruise outside.

Now or never, while the elevating operation takes place. No excitement: "excitement makes your needle lose the North." Only a more tense readiness to grasp the first indication of the mystery.

Floodlights beat on the stone walls. The slender, pointed, wicked-looking craft advanced slowly between them to a point where she must rise to the next level to proceed.

And then eyes and ears seized the answer, like terriers who have waited patiently for a woodchuck to pop out of his hole.

A uniformed officer passed along the gangway on top of the wall, and entered a low dome-shaped structure, a third of the way along the lock.

"All or nothing," I resolved.

So, wondering at each step if I would drop into

some hole and plunge over my head, I cautiously advanced to a point opposite the window in this dome, and not over ten or fifteen paces away.

I looked directly into a brilliantly lighted little control room. The engineer-lieutenant was there, handling levers. There was boiling and rushing of water. Gradually the masts of the vessel began to rise. At the end of seven or eight minutes she had lifted to the higher level.

More lever work. But I did not need to wait longer. I understood everything. I could draw a plan from memory, placing that control chamber correctly. I knew exactly what the mechanical and electrical system was.

My Information was secured.

Naturally that was not all. That Information and I were out in the water, between guards on the lock and patrols on shore. What had been accomplished meant nothing unless I could get away with my mental booty.

Very slowly I worked back to the sheltering rushes. Then I headed toward a spot half way between where two sentry beats met. Even this gentle movement was welcome after those motionless hours.

The patrols did not speak as they came to their respective boundaries, but the beat of their feet told me each moment where they were.

At last one sentry was relieved. The new man stopped for a few seconds to mutter something to the other. He had hardly started again when I was ashore, and creeping up the bank into the close tongue of woods.

I crawled like a snake—and kept on crawling till I was far out of hearing.

Reaching the outskirts of that town, I started at once on foot for the nearest large city, where my orders bade me deliver what I had secured to our nation's representative.

It was only a job, like a hundred others. I, and every other man in our corps, have been in many tighter places, places where it came flatly to a case of kill or be killed. Yet after thirty years I can still hear the *lap-lap* of those cold little waves, can see that officer throwing his revealing lever, can feel the briars and stubs that raked me mercilessly as I bellied my way up from that deadly shore to the safe woods.

I fancy a man in such work must, during the crises he learns to meet so stolidly, have many emotions subconsciously of which he is not even aware.

It is stating exact truth to record that in this instance, as in many others, I had no real sense of fear or excitement.

I knew death and disgrace were at my elbow. They might take one by the throat at any moment. The same thing is true of driving a motorcar in city traffic: you look at it calmly, recognize it, are supremely confident of your ability to control each situation.

Certainly there is no flutter of nerves, no perceptible acceleration of heartbeat. It must be that habit and will have learned to check these panicky ideas at birth, to isolate them from the motor centres.

For something must happen down inside a man. Something vital enough to make a deep dent in his memory.

Otherwise he would not be able, as I find myself, to run off one such "forgotten" incident after another, in all its vivid detail, just as if he put a motion-picture reel in the projector.

One whiff of the heavy smell of black harbor mud still starts such pictures in my mind.

CHAPTER X

Some Peacetime Excursions

LOOKING BACK NOW AT THAT DECADE PRECEDING the World War, it is easy for anybody to see that every nation was feverishly busy, preparing for the inevitable explosion.

Encouraged by a general European peace which had stretched unbroken for a third of a century, the idealists were happily announcing the arrival of true international civilization. Enthusiasts like W. T. Stead portrayed the "United States of Europe" as an imminent development of the new understanding and cooperation between nations.

A final argument that war was a thing of the past seemed to be that science had produced new engines of destruction, on land, on sea, in the air, which made war too horrible to contemplate—reasoning that might well have aroused a philosopher's scepticism. What men do springs from what they are. Not vice versa.

I make no claim to special knowledge in that controversy, long engaging great minds, as to whether or no this odd creature, man, will eventually outgrow the stupid and barbaric habit of war-making, in which he has indulged at intervals ever since his appearance on this planet. But I can state that if he does, it will not be because he has acquired the powers to do it more efficiently and devastatingly. Nor for any other external reason. Only through some gradual inner change in the very essence of the creature.

We, at least, who worked on the inside from 1903 to 1913 could have no such illusions. If a human being could have looked down into the earth below the volcano of Krakatoa in 1883; if he could have seen all those subterranean forces gathering—vast masses of molten matter, radioactive materials ready when disturbed to release their devastating energy, metals that "go mad" in water, rivers and reservoirs of water ready to flow into the hell-brew—he would not have been much impressed by the fact that Krakatoa had been inactive for two centuries.

While we active ones obeyed orders blindly, the mighty clanking in the forges of Mars was ever in our ears.

We knew all about the rapidly waxing armies and navies, the new and terrible engines of destruction. Our lives were spent in furnishing our own country with the latest exact details of these grim preparations all about us. Given men as they were, and are, those prodigious powers had to be used sooner or later.

All that was not our business. Our days and nights, and fullest energies of mind and body, were devoted to meeting a succession of deliberately invoked personal crises. To carry out orders successfully and stay alive gave a man all he needed to think about.

More than once I have smiled, a bit wryly, at hearing some reader of spy-romances pronounce our work exciting. "Think of having such thrills day by day!" one young woman put it.

Doubtless, from a certain point of view such underground adventures as we are bound to be involved in are exciting. But the agent himself has no part in the thrill. It has been often pointed out that no traveller finds adventure unless he takes it with him. And a secret agent who started with that quick emotional response would not last long.

No. I felt no excitement, no thrill, no elation, almost no fear. I went at those missions with the practicality of a hardware dealer. My early training had made me self-contained, uncommunicative, completely unemotional; this had been deliberately developed into a wary suspicion of any stranger. I could not speak of what concerned me most even to a best friend. So I had no friends.

I loved no woman: that emotion could not flourish in such soil. I rarely drank anything but a glass of wine. I had given up smoking, because in emergencies it was a handicap. The life was lonely and prosaic.

We were workmen, doing a series of hard, mean, dangerous, unrelated jobs. There was no credit or praise for success—merely prompt dismissal for failure. We violated all the normal decent human instincts, under orders. Almost daily we took our lives and reputations in our hands—

certain of being disowned and abandoned to our fate if things went wrong.

We were well aware of more extreme cases, where an agent, secretly condemned as treacherous by his hidden superiors, had been deliberately sent to certain betrayal—that his execution might come from the enemy instead of his employers. There was a deftness, an ironic fitness, about that which satisfied the minds of the organized realists who ruled our destiny.

Yet we were inspired and bound together by a common devotion which I have rarely seen equalled. The French call it *esprit de corps*. Inadequate as it sounds in words, that sense of professional obligation, doing one's job, seems to be among the most dominant of a man's impulses.

Our only reward lay in satisfying a deep pride in the achievements of our bureau. Merely to continue a member of that organization was a sort of decoration. As I look back I find myself often amazed at the impossibilities we active men accomplished under the spur of that rather impersonal urge.

Only men whose personal feelings had been extirpated, who had become unbelievably mechanized, could have compiled such a record.

Devoid of emotions as I became while exercising my trade, I realize to-day I do get some excitement when I look back at a few of those incidents.

I was ordered to one of the world's capitals. I was to get the latest secret codes of that army. Also, if practicable, some highly confidential reports which our people knew to be at headquarters. There were in addition sketches of a new device, and a mobilization plan which would not be unwelcome.

Those were staples in my strange business. Generally you bought them from some poor devil of a clerk, from an assistant technician, from a professional dealer in such contraband. The rates were fairly well established by the importance of the material—often modified by the necessities of the underhand seller.

It was quite customary to haggle over price like any pair of Hebrew junkmen, to whom this contest of wits beats a poker game, beats even the money saved. And a bargainer is severely handicapped when he knows, and the buyer knows, that pressing debts force him to sell quickly. So there is apt to be a great deal of quiet study of background before such a transaction is begun.

I arrived and consulted our own confidential people stationed in that city. They could give me no lead whatever. My own cautious inquiries, too, failed to bring to light any obviously venal official in that particular section of the war department.

It looked as if burglary were indicated, instead of the easier bribery.

So I laid an elaborate plan to help ourselves to the documents we wanted.

First of all I disappeared from the local scene—nothing to cause remark in the case of a minor, migratory attaché. He had simply gone to another post.

But the very next day there was a new window-washer and general handyman in that war department building. A discerning eye that had paused for careful scrutiny would have detected strange resemblances between this cleaner and Agent Number 7. No such eye took the trouble. Nobody was interested in this humble addition to the cleaning force.

Thenceforth I could work from the inside. Except through some extraordinary accident, this job was bound to take time. I did not make the mistake of being anything but a window-washer for the first few weeks.

However, for one special purpose I did have to risk giving myself a measure of individualization. Those windows were cleaned as they had never been before. When the plumbing went wrong one day, the new handyman located the trouble and fixed it before the office heads had received any complaint. Which gave my immediate superior implicit confidence in my character.

That was the initial step.

Next, by branching out into fields not properly in my domain, and doing three men's work, it was not difficult to convince this functionary that it would be advantageous all round for me to have a helper.

By a happy chance I knew just the man—who was momentarily unemployed.

Thus with ease and naturalness I secured the presence of the special assistant I needed alongside of me for this particular problem.

This was my friend Jules, one of the most entertaining scoundrels with whom I have ever associated. (And my word! That would be a choice collection!) His nature and training almost predestined him for the technical work he was to perform for me.

Originally, I believe, Jules was a Frenchman. But his origins had been so completely erased by years of violent contacts that he had become a citizen of the world.

During his novitiate, he had worked in a factory producing safes. His natural gift for mechanics was extraordinary: he became a skilled workman, who seemed able to make the tumblers of those particular locks sit up and beg. Realizing he was wasting his talents at this monotonous job of manufacturing, he retired, to use his acquired skill in a more profitable business of his own—taking a rigorous post-graduate course in safes of all makes as he came upon them, until there were few which he could not persuade without recourse to raw violence.

His own country failed to appreciate his genius; perhaps he had merely not found the right field in which to exercise it. In any case, he shook off the dust of his ungrateful native land in a speedy, secret departure. After an odyssey of which I got startling glimpses at unexpected moments, he arrived within our borders; and some alert scout of our Service, perceiving how handy a human tool this might be on occasions, recommended him to my superior.

He had achieved the most complete internationalism. Naturally, he took some extra pleasure in tricking his native land, which he felt had persecuted him because he was cleverer than others; but, except for a good-natured liking for myself, he would just as readily have worked against us as for us. Though insisting on his high pay, he was dominated not so much by the money as the desire to display his startling professional skill.

Jules was unique—a combination of superhuman mechanic and cold-blooded apache. During a job his purchased loyalty could be depended on to the limit. I have known few men more satisfactory to have around when one of those sudden life-and-death situations broke.

This precious helper had eyes and ears all over him, and with the advantage of our inside position we studied every detail of the office and personnel. In spite of our joint efforts, it took nearly three months of this spying from beneath to be sure of the necessary facts.

The codes, and a lot of other interesting papers, were in a wall-safe, in the corner office belonging to the Captain who was chief of that bureau. We knew that office inside and out. We knew the make and date of the safe. We had checked minutely the daily habits of this officer custodian, of every clerk, secretary and messenger.

At last I was ready. The plan was complete. There was an alternative at every point where trouble might rise.

Late that afternoon the Captain left. We knew

exactly where he was going. The force began to depart, the more important functionaries first, as usual. With our buckets and mops, my safe-cracker pal and I went into the corner office.

Instead of starting in to clean, we hid in the little coat closet of the ante-room, leaving the door ajar.

The last insignificant stragglers hurried away from the big outer room. The lights went out. Silence settled down upon the deserted range of the war department quarters.

We reconnoitred cautiously. Nobody. The whole place belonged to us.

Noiselessly we stole back through the ante-room to the inner office. We needed no light to avoid desk and chairs, to show us the spot where the safe waited: we had a mental diagram of every object in that room.

Like any expert when his professional moment comes, my apache did not waste a moment in words. In an instant he was in front of the safe door, had lighted a fat, stubby plumber's candle, was manipulating the knob, his head turned to it, listening intently.

As I watched the tense absorption of his strong, reckless face in the dim candle-light, I was reminded of a favorite pointer, "freezing" to the hot scent of an unseen partridge just ahead. I almost expected to see his jaws work convulsively, and the drool run out as that statuesque hunting dog's used to do in such a tense moment.

Jules' face might have been cast in bronze. Those spatulate craftsmen's fingers twirled this way and that. Then there was a sudden twitch of the jaw muscles beneath this mask. His straining ear had caught what he was expecting.

I began to congratulate myself on the preparation which had led to such smooth success. For the fingers were flying faster and faster. The problem must be solved. Any instant now I would see swing wide this iron door which was the last obstacle to my search.

And just then something happened. I had no idea what it was that disturbed my concentration, but my head automatically jerked around.

In spite of his absorption Jules' animal instincts were quicker than mine. Before I could stretch out my arm to warn him, his great hairy hand smothered the candle.

We crouched there in the darkness, holding our breath. Another sound came, distinct now—the noise of the far door being closed in the outer office. All at once I found my deadly little automatic gripped in my left hand.

Steps echoed along that big, empty outer room. They came closer and closer. We could not so much as whisper to each other. We knew we were both ready. That had to be sufficient.

The inner door was pushed open. Walking confidently, the unseen, inopportune visitor stepped straight to the desk. The light there flashed on.

It was the uniformed officer in charge of that bureau. He had forgotten something—and our bad luck, or his, had made him return for it.

As the light fell on his startled face and waxed mustache points, it also gleamed on a pair of brass knuckles, evidently kept on his desk as a paperweight.

I was nearest. I jumped him before his wits were fully functioning—and got in that disabling blow with the side of the rigid hand upon the windpipe.

Automatically, however, he had seized the brass knuckles at the first alarm; his roundhouse swipe at me caught me over the eye, tearing the flesh away so that the whole brow hung down. The blood gushed out, blinding me.

My companion got in one shrewd blow as the luckless officer fell. But that was really not needed.

Something more grim though was needed.

He had seen too much, this poor devil. And I would be a marked man for some time.

Jules looked at me questioningly. I could merely shrug my shoulders. He knew the answer as well as I.

Only one thing to do. We gave him a prick with a poisoned thorn, put out the light, and continued our work.

It took some minutes in the toilet for the first-aid treatment of my gashed temple. The instant this was roughly bandaged so I could see and not drip blood about, Jules was back at the safe. The interruption had come at the moment of success.

Almost immediately he swung the door open. I searched the contents swiftly.

There were the codes, which were most important. The other documents had evidently been removed, but there was little sense of failure as I bundled up a few papers that looked interesting, with the main prize.

Now to get away with it. This unforeseen mischance spurred us to haste.

One swift glance at the prostrate figure showed that the poison had done its work. The scent of the Jose Maria Farina cologne he had used still hung heavy in the air.

Extinguishing the candle, we stole silently out through the dark and deserted rooms.

Creeping down the staircase one flight, we crossed the corresponding office on the floor below. It was too risky to use the street entrance. A side window on this second floor seemed a better chance.

I looked out.

There was a pale moon shining now and then between the driving masses of dark clouds. The walls of the ornate old building had all sorts of ornaments, ledges and projections, which a trained climber could use.

Waiting for a period when the moon was behind clouds, I climbed out on the window-sill and swung myself into space, holding by a heavy sculptured shield, and thanking heaven for the baroque architecture whose virtues I had never before perceived.

In a few seconds I was on the sidewalk, huddled in the shadow against the wall, and searching the street in both directions. Nothing stirred.

Jules came down like a monkey, grinning in delight.

"We make a team, Captain," he whispered.

"You know where the car is?"

"You can bet a month's pay on that."

"Go around the block that way. We'll meet there."

"Yes, safer to separate. I'll beat you to it."

He seemed to melt out of sight. Wiping some drops of blood from my eye, I walked the opposite way as quickly as I dared.

There was no hitch. Presently we stood beside

my car, which was drawn up in a badly lighted spot, the engine purring softly.

My splendid driver had the door open. We ducked inside. Hardly had we touched the seat, when the powerful car shot ahead.

He was a grand fellow, that driver, an exiled Alsatian. The car was exceptionally swift and silent for those days, and he loved it as if it were his child. When excited he would talk to the engine, soothing or encouraging it.

I heard him now almost crooning as we sped rapidly along unfrequented streets.

Sooner than I had thought possible we were safely out of the city. Then his tone changed, and he really opened it up. At times we were speeding along highways about as fast as I had ever travelled. Then he would whisk off into some deserted sideroad, leave that for another, finally swing back again to the main highway.

Before dawn we were at the border.

There was no trouble. Our passports were in order. I managed to cover up my bandaged head. And that smiling Alsatian chauffeur could joke the sleepiest guards into grinning good humor. (Later on, poor chap, he was taken behind the enemy lines and summarily shot.)

Next day the codes which had cost a life were delivered to my superior. A surgeon plastered the cut on my forehead.

I was ready for another assignment.

I cannot recall that I experienced any special pangs of regret for that officer who had to be killed. Not that I enjoyed killing. That man who was I seems to me now to have been a person of rather more than normal good-will toward his fellow humans.

But when that necessity arose it was something a man had to take in his stride. Any squeamishness at the time, or morbidity afterwards, would have disqualified a man completely. It was imperative to acquire a thorough, emotionless practicality: certain things were to be accomplished; whatever stood in the way was to be removed. The human animal seems able to adjust his mind to anything, when he accepts it as essential.

As a craftsman I was interested in the perfect

working of my poisoned thorn. Through all my years as an agent, that was one of only two occasions when I had to use that particular deadly implement.

There were other situations, however, when it became obligatory to resort to even more primitive weapons. One in particular I recall, because of several highly unusual features.

In Bucharest, on a short furlough, I had become acquainted with an agent of a country completely friendly to ours. He was a likable, clean, efficient fellow, with a delightful vein of quiet humor. Temperamentally and professionally, truly intimate friends were not for me; yet I took considerable pleasure from his company. I realized he must know what I was, just as I had plenty of private information about him. We never mentioned these matters.

Orders came, and we separated. Of course neither gave the slightest hint of where he was going next.

My assignment was striking enough—to make a

full report on the coast defenses of a fortified Oriental port.

Though quite hardened to missions whose reasons and sequences I could not understand, I did permit myself some inner surprise at these instructions. No stretch of the fancy could visualize an invasion of that country. If I were to be snuffed out, I really had a distinct preference for having it come while attempting to get something worth while.

However— Orders. Perhaps it was simply the collector's urge: if our brass hats had everything else in the way of fortified ports, those plans might become in their minds as important as a unique imperforate to a postage stamp collector. At least this long expedition ought to furnish me with some new character details, of people quite different from those about whom I had accumulated so many facts—observing the tendency of these facts to group themselves into quite definite categories. From the special point of view I had to use, I had found men surprisingly alike, instead of eternally different.

I reached my destination. As an insignificant, idle tourist, I made some preliminary observations.

A mountain range reared itself behind the city. From some point up that wild hillside all the harbor fortifications should lie in plain view. An understanding eye, gazing down from that spot, could diagram the complete system.

That was all right—but there proved to be difficulties in carrying out this logical idea.

Next morning I strolled along the excellent road twisting up the hillside, picking out several tree-covered shoulders just above the lower precipices, which would apparently serve my purpose.

Rounding a sharp turn, I was confronted by a frowning sentry, rifle in hand. I could not understand his words, but there was no mistaking what he meant to convey: I must go no further.

Returning, I made casual inquiries. That entire upper area was prohibited to visitors. All the roads were strictly guarded.

It seemed to me I ought to be able to reach my chosen lookout without passing these road patrols. Next morning I made the attempt.

Some distance below the post where I had been halted, I left the road, plunged into the thick scrub, and painfully worked my way on a slanting course up toward the elevated shelf I had noticed. Below it the mountainside fell off sheer for some hundreds of feet to the narrow sandy beach of the bay.

As I cautiously wriggled through the last thickets between me and my vantage-point, I suddenly caught a glimpse of a human figure ahead. Dropping down out of sight, I peered out. The stranger was almost concealed in a clump of stunted pines, just at the spot I was making for.

Having come this far, I had to find out what he was doing. With all the stealth I could manage I wormed my way toward him, crawling through the open spaces, keeping some cover always between us.

Just as I decided I was close enough to rush him, I was amazed to see he was using a camera—on those very fortifications I meant to sketch and photograph.

My surprise must have made me careless. A dry twig cracked under my knee.

The man whirled about, drawing a pistol with one swift, easy motion. Then he saw my startled face peering through the leaves.

It was Frank, my Bucharest friend, on the same mission as I!

The meeting was so ludicrous, after our recent secretive parting, that we broke into mutual restrained laughter.

Then we chucked away custom and tradition and foregathered on this job. We compared notes, exposed films, made sketches, revised each other's estimates of distances, finished our joint aerial survey. By that time it had gotten on to perhaps four in the afternoon. We started back together, well pleased with our day.

We had covered about quarter of the distance back to the lower road when we heard a crashing in the bushes ahead.

Evidently a sentry had seen something suspicious and was coming to investigate.

Motioning with his hand, my companion sank out of sight behind a mass of thick growth. I ran to conceal myself as best I could on the other side of the little clear space in which we were standing.

The crashing sounds drew nearer, interspersed with explosive words as some stub raked the clumsy sentry in a tender place. He was forcing his way straight through the tangle with bull-like obstinacy.

Presently he broke through close by me, hot, sweaty and much out of humor. He was bound to see me. I stood up. We stared at each other.

He jabbered angrily. I still could not understand a word, but the sign language of his gun was all too clear. He was in a state of mind where it would have relieved him to thrust several inches of that shiny bayonet into my anatomy.

To hold his attention, I stepped toward him, talking loudly and gesticulating.

My quick-witted companion needed no prompting. The suspicious guard stepped back, levelling his rifle at me threateningly.

And at that instant Frank sprang from his hiding place, and seized the man with a strangle-hold. Then, taking a firm grip, he swung him over his shoulder. Presently he had him face down on the ground, his strong fingers squeezing the captive's throat threateningly.

The rifle had flown through the air and crashed among the bushes. The sentry, taken too suddenly to make any outcry, gurgled but hardly struggled. He had not so much as seen Frank. I fancy he was quite sure one of the many demons who infest those parts had him in a fatal clasp.

No help for it now. And we must both share in the unpleasant finality.

It is amazing how completely one strong emotion can drive out all others. I was conscious of no pity or hesitation. It was merely a dirty job to be finished as quickly as possible. Frank and I gave each other one glance which said everything.

I grasped the poor groaning creature on one side, Frank on the other. His superstitious terror was so extreme he did not dare open his eyes.

We swung him between us twice like a pendulum.

Then, with a mighty heave, we hurled him over the precipice.

Dropping flat, we peered over the brink down

that dizzy drop. We saw the body bounce far out from a slanting projection, saw it turn over twice, saw it land on the boulders down below.

That was the end of that. We stayed not on the order of our going from that place.

For two weeks we lay doggo at the house of one of Frank's compatriots.

We heard the authorities were making the most strenuous efforts to penetrate the mystery. All they knew was that this soldier had been found thoroughly smashed up at the base of the cliff, where he could not have fallen without being far off his beat. His rifle was discovered up on the hillside. There was no plausible explanation. Our part in the occurrence was never suspected.

When the military excitement had died down, we got away—and separated, as uncommunicative as before concerning our future plans.

But there was an extra pressure in our final handshake, as we wished each other "good hunting."

CHAPTER XI

BUYING MEN

"BUT, CAPTAIN, YOU ARE A COMPLETE cynic," exclaimed a charming woman neighbor at a dinner table. I had made what I considered a most obvious comment on the personalities involved in a sensational affair being discussed.

"At least, madame, I am cynical in your sense about these labels and definitions we accept so blindly."

"He's quite right," put in the professor. "Those original Cynics, those Greek philosophers who first adopted the dog emblem, were fanatics for truth at any cost. They were a harsh wind blowing away all pompous humbug. Naturally the people who were fat and gross with humbug had to discredit them."

"I confess I like to think of myself rather as a realist," I said. "Though that may strike you as more cynical than anything I've said. Truth is always the most interesting thing."

"If you can get enough of it," remarked the scholar.

He had a point there which made me reflect, as I considered my own career.

I can perceive that my profession necessarily has an attitude exactly opposite to that of Diogenes looking for an honest man. We must find a few incorruptible humans who can be trained to do the work of our own inner band of investigators; but, when that trusted organization is once formed, it must trust nobody outside. On the contrary, it has to search all over the world for men who can be bought.

I take no responsibility for the world of men. I did not create them. I have used them as I found them, to do the job which came my way to do, to serve my country in accordance with my orders.

For I was born, and have lived, a soldier.

There might be a shrewd question as to whether my efforts left certain individuals in worse case than if I had never met them. That discussion would speedily land one in a hopeless tangle of conflicting moralities, of just how lofty and impersonal an end must be to justify any means.

They did not teach us anything of that irresolute sort in our training school.

Considering it now, with complete readiness to accept the truth, I doubt if I ever "corrupted" any such individual. I did take great pains to find those whose weakness had been already corrupted by conditions. Those I made use of, as a commonplace, everyday part of our routine task.

Again a practical mind like mine disclaims ultimate responsibility. I was proud to be a man under authority. I was proud to be able to obey orders to the limit.

As a matter of cold working fact, during thirty-odd years' experience, I have never found a man I needed to buy whom I failed in purchasing. Some come much higher than others. The price may be other than money. But there is always a price.

I can see you, Reader, who may have followed me up to this point, draw back at that, incredulous. You are doubtless visualizing some honorable tough-fibred independent friend, whom you know could never be bribed. Or, in a closer *argumentum ad hominem*, you are asserting your own inner conviction that *you* could never betray your country for money.

Granted. And my congratulations.

But my statement was applied specifically to those I needed to buy. The men who could furnish or filch the facts and documents we were after were almost always underpaid bureaucrats, or men with a grudge, who felt themselves unfairly treated by an impersonal government.

I sometimes think we expect an incredible return of integrity and loyalty for the salaries we pay bank clerks and confidential government employees—in spite of the fact that I am convinced the average normal person much prefers to be honest, and is highly uncomfortable when he is forced into something else.

Government employees in the military branches, especially heads of minor bureaus, seem always unable to live on their salaries. Debt is a chronic disease with them.

Military tailors in various countries have related confidentially how their bills for uniforms go unpaid for years; they are lucky in some cases if a sub-lieutenant's first purchases are cleaned up by the time he is a colonel.

The technical men and the small executives are in the same boat. With mysterious unanimity they have testified privately that their "necessary" expenses are just 27 per cent more than they receive in salary. When you are rolling up a snowball of unpaid accounts, which increases each year by a quarter of all you spend, you are apt to find this engrossing most of your attention.

These men are not independent. Far from it.

They are daily going through the degrading process of trying to curry personal or political favor, in order to hold a job, or get a better one. Meanwhile creditors are to be placated with partial payments, staved off somehow. Years of that will blunt any man's finer sensibilities. Frequently he becomes so demoralized he is ready for any escape from this incessant, agonizing pressure.

For these are men with some little official position to maintain, whose children must go to the right schools, who must entertain occasionally, whose wives must be properly dressed at formal functions. They are almost inevitably forced into debt. And a man irretrievably in debt can no longer afford the bright jewel of honor.

Hence the incongruous fact that the higher the official's position, the easier he is to buy—and the cheaper. He is harder pressed. He cannot afford to bargain. I doubt if there is a man in a million who will not break somewhere under the steady relentless torture of hopeless financial pressure.

Perhaps it marks me as having developed into something coldly subhuman, nevertheless, I am relating exact truth. So let it be recorded that I took an acute clinical interest in the reactions of these unfortunates to the idea of possible relief from their difficulties.

That close study of motive and behavior was necessary to evolve a successful technique. I did evolve one. It worked.

In an important case it was usually simple to pick out some key man who must be reached.

Before meeting this prospect I made a careful study of his character and background, far more exhaustive than the report a financial investigator would secure for a credit-rating agency like Dun & Bradstreet. Unobtrusively I gathered items from his family, his acquaintances, his office associates, his bank, his creditors, our sub-agents, everywhere.

When we came together I knew more about that man's antecedents, finances, personal peculiarities and official prospects than he knew himself.

The talk at first would be about anything entertaining. An amusing story, a piece of gossip, a rumor he hadn't heard always helped to establish an easy atmosphere. Gradually, smilingly, I would begin to complain about the high cost of everything, the impossibility of living on an official salary. That always brought a sympathetic response. Then would come the general topic of financial gain, lucky people who made a lot quickly by some fortunate coup.

All through this I would be watching his eyes. Also the muscles of his cheek and jaw. If I caught a certain flash in the eye, if those muscles gave an involuntary twitch as a certain idea sank in—I knew he was ready.

When it came to actual negotiation, his eyes would never meet mine squarely. Always he would look away. But I learned to know from his expression when the amount mentioned was sufficient.

If he belonged to that well-defined species without the odd courage to do a disgraceful thing at the first real chance, I would drop the subject and take my departure, leaving him to himself for a week or two.

Only too well I knew I had in his money troubles a persistent ally, who from within would argue on my side, morning, noon and night. Almost always it was he who brought about the next meeting. The rest was easy.

Especially if he broke into protests, at the first suggestion that I was in the market for something he could furnish—when he cried out he was an honest man, when he asserted his patriotism, when he declared he could never look his family and friends in the face if he did such a thing—then I knew I had merely to name the figure.

Of course, some of this variety carried their cowardly hypocrisy, or caution, so far that I could not deal with them directly. The bargain must be struck, the delivery made, through an alter ego, what those Frenchmen call an *âme damnée*.

It was all the same.

There were cases where a seller had little difficulty in building up that self-justification at which the human mind is so ingenious.

Take this incident.

I once bought the complete drawings for a new and greatly improved elevating mechanism for the shells of big guns. I bought them for $20,000 from the inventors, two keen young engineers in a government department. If I named the country, you would undoubtedly pronounce me a slanderous liar. Those two technicians would have been indignant had anyone charged them with a lack of patriotism.

This was the story.

They were alert, enthusiastic young engineers with an inventive turn. Getting this idea, they worked it out together, in their own time, sketching, testing, making models.

When it was right, they showed it to a superior official in their branch.

"I really think you two have got something," he declared. And he sent it along to a higher-up.

At last, after passing from one group of experts to another, the new device reached the top. It received the august approval of the highest.

The two inventors were summoned by the good-natured superior.

"Good news for you," he announced. "The Government is going to adopt that dinkus of yours officially. It's a feather in your caps, and a credit to our bureau."

The two looked at each other.

"That's fine," said the older. "But I say, Chief—"

"What's wrong now?"

"How about a bit of royalty to us? Joseph and I have been most awfully strapped ever since we got married—that stuff about two living as cheap as one is the bunk. We're mighty glad to have the

Government use that invention, but a little royalty would look awful good to both of us."

The superior was no longer good-humored.

"I'm surprised at you. Haven't you any patriotic feeling at all? You know everything you do belongs to the Government. You ought to be proud that the heads down there think enough of your invention to adopt it."

There could be no argument. But those two young technicians were utterly convinced the Government owed them money for their idea.

When I got a private tip from a sub-agent and approached them, they received me with open arms, as a providential dispenser of essential justice. They had access to the files: I soon had two complete sets of the drawings.

After all, they reasoned, they were only selling their own.

There were other kinds. I learned something from the Ingenious Colonel.

Through an alert sub-agent I discovered that an elderly noble Colonel, occupying a position of confidence in his country's war department, was ready to sell detailed plans of that country's whole system of fortifications. He was pressed for time, as he would soon retire. He insisted on negotiating directly with a responsible Service representative. The price was $20,000, cash on delivery.

I met him in a private conference. I did not like his looks, but we could hardly quarrel with the kind of person we were forced to use for such purposes. He clearly did have those plans. We wanted them. There would be no payment till he delivered them to me personally. It looked all right.

We arranged on a distant meeting place, and the deal was agreed upon.

All the time some instinct was warning me. Perhaps it was the way he spoke of his "honor." However, I had had an unbroken run of successes without a hitch; my confidence made me disregard this inner monitor.

The truth was that this ingenious Colonel had worked out in his mind a neat double-cross, by which he planned to retain money, plans and "honor." His idea had the simplicity of greatness: once alone with me in some remote spot, I with the

$20,000, he with the plans, he would kill me and carry off everything. No one but himself would ever know. I suspect he already knew things about himself which made this betrayal of a prying outsider seem venial enough. It could even be presented as a patriotic outwitting of an enemy.

The transaction was to be completed far away from both our headquarters, down on the Adriatic coast near Brindisi. I was to come alone (his honor again), he likewise.

"A personal matter between two gentlemen," was his idea of it.

I journeyed to the agreed small town, quite unsuspicious of what I was walking into. For once I underestimated an opponent.

Well outside the town limits there was a lonely house whose occupant was one of my sub-agents. I made my way there under the cheerless sky of a late afternoon. For a storm was brewing. According to instructions, my local man was not in sight.

I waited awhile in the front room of the rather sordid dwelling. It was dirty, the wallpaper torn and grimy. Then I heard rapid footsteps outside.

The Colonel came in swiftly. He was shrouded in a great military cape.

He looked about nervously.

"Are we alone?" he asked in a hoarse whisper.

"You see, Excellency," said I, waving my arm about the bare room.

"I cannot delay a moment. I am taking terrible risks. Let us finish. Here are the plans. The money."

I stepped forward, the package of large notes in my outstretched right hand, reaching with my left for the large envelope I expected.

It was what he had counted on.

With a quick jerk he drew from inside his cape, not the plans but a slung shot—and in one smooth motion he struck with all his force.

Luckily, he was too eager. The blow was a glancing one on my forehead. Otherwise I should never have had a chance to tell about it.

Taken quite by surprise, however, I was knocked down. That former wound was torn open. Between the blood in my eyes and the stunning effect of the blow, I was momentarily helpless. He had me at his mercy. Through the fog I had a glimpse of his vain smile of satisfaction as he deliberately drew a pistol.

I decided my number was up. I knew I deserved it for my careless over-confidence.

But fortunately my local man was not of a trustful nature. He had taken no chances either way, and had been watching us at a cunning hole in the wall of the back room, concealed by a loose flap of figured wallpaper.

He saw the attack, rushed to the door. In the nick of time he levelled a pistol, fitted with a silencer, and shot the Colonel through the heart.

It was an odd experience to lie there, helpless at that crucial moment, expecting each instant to feel a bullet—and then to hear the slight *phht* of the explosion, and behold that officer sprawl forward on the floor almost at my feet.

The Colonel had provided all the properties for his engaging little comedy. The real plans we were to buy were in a pouch inside his cape.

For once they cost us less than we had figured. For I personally never had less regret for any dirty work inseparable from my missions than when I looked at the still distorted face of this aristocratic scoundrel.

As for my efficient sub-agent, a shrewd native of those parts, when he heard what his reward would be, he was more than satisfied with the afternoon's entertainment.

The problem of disposing of the Colonel's body gave him no concern whatever.

Indeed, I had the impression that on those terms casual killings could not come along too frequently for his taste.

My own sensations were quite different.

At least, though, I had had a lesson I should never need twice. The last thing I should have imagined was disaster coming to me through over-trustfulness. After that humiliating experience, suspicion of everybody became a first instinct.

CHAPTER XII

WAR

ON JUNE 28, 1914, THE AUSTRIAN HEIR, Crown Prince Franz Ferdinand and his lovely commoner wife were assassinated at Sarajevo by a young Bosnian Serb, Gavrilo Princip. Princip and his companion represented the extreme irresponsible terrorist element in that conspiratorial South Slav movement which patched-up Austria-Hungary had so long repressed, as a condition of imperial existence.

To those of us who lived and had our being underground, that came more as an anticipated fulfilment than a surprise. No one could have predicted the precise moment or nature of the first outburst. But the locality was almost obviously predestined. For centuries the Balkans had been the bubbling pot where mighty opposing forces met beneath the surface, and heated each other to angry incandescence.

We were not deceived by the false superficial calm of the ensuing weeks. All too clearly this tragic incident was the puff of steam from the crater, heralding the volcano's titanic explosion.

A generation which knew War only from histories was about to feel the dragon's fiery breath.

In theory we were ready for whatever came. From the first moment of my introduction to the Service, I had comprehended that our hand-picked little band was a skeleton organization, capable of instant and indefinite expansion to meet the increased stresses of war.

I doubt though if even our most far-sighted and experienced chiefs anticipated the volume and variety of those demands as they instantly poured upon us. It did not take long to perceive that this was a world struggle to the limit; the very existence of the great nations was involved; and, as when an individual faces life and death, every conceivable resource of men, money, science and imagination must be tossed into the scales.

The content of the term "military intelligence" expanded suddenly till it darkened the sky of human knowledge; and every secret service proliferated madly to include organizations for handling censorship, propaganda, counter-espionage, sabotage, war trade data, and a hundred other matters formerly outside their bailiwicks.

England had brought about a root-and-branch reorganization of army administration in 1907, following the Esher report on the lessons of the Boer War. An up-to-date intelligence department was developed as part of the General Staff. An admirable training-school was established. The most eminent member of the organization was General Baden-Powell, in some respects the ace of all modern spies. There was a centre of counter-espionage at Berne, Switzerland, under General Cockerill, and headquarters were set up in Rotterdam and Amsterdam. They did excellent work. Oddly enough, at times their agents exhibited an almost schoolboyish sense of humor which proved peculiarly baffling, for example to the Germans—who had constructed their service with their usual solemn thoroughness, efficiency and grim discipline.

The French Deuxième Bureau was universally

accepted as the finest in the world, up to the time of the Dreyfus affair. They had recovered from that shock and were among the best when war broke. Critics have maintained that the initial disaster of 1914 resulted from faulty interpretation of intelligence by the French staff, but there were no criticisms of the field work.

There were two opposing schools of thought when it came to interpretation. The older was that the function of spies was to gather facts enabling the strategists to work intelligently along a theory already formed. Thus, it is charged the French theorists assumed as a certainty that only first-line German troops would start the assault: what they needed was exact reports identifying the enemy army corps being moved up to the front line. Their whole plan was based on that.

However, the truth proved to be that the Germans had injected duplicate army corps of reserves with the same numbers as these first-line divisions. So, instead of the 40 divisions of shock troops they expected, the French armies encountered 68 divisions.

Nothing could be better calculated than that object lesson to add firsthand "interpretation" as a prime function of Intelligence.

It was phrased concisely: "The Intelligence Officer's job is to command the enemy's army. The less he knows about his own, the better."

This elevated the Intelligence Chief's responsibility to something like parity with that of the Commander-in-Chief or the Chief of the General Staff. Men of the most brilliant capacity were called to these higher posts.

General Dupont, who organized the Polish service, and the heads of the Russian Ochranyat were such outstanding figures.

The Russian bureau (later the Cheka, then the Gay-Pay-Oo) worked in close cooperation with the French service, operating from Switzerland, Copenhagen, Stockholm, Warsaw, even Germany itself.

If one could get together the inside stories from all these services on both sides, it would make a tale beyond the imaginations of all the romancers.

Though the War added new tools like wireless

and aeroplanes, there was really little difference in the work of field agents like myself. There were some new ways of getting killed—but there had always been enough of those to prevent the novelties from seeming particularly impressive.

Early in 1916 I received an assignment somewhat out of the ordinary.

Grand Duke Nicholas of Russia had been displaced the summer before from the supreme command on the Austrian front and put in charge of the faraway Caucasus district.

His skill and energy had transformed the stalemate on that front to a series of Russian victories. Capturing the key city of Erzerum, and sweeping on to ancient Trebizond, on the southern shore of the Black Sea, he presented a growing menace to hard-pressed Turkey.

Enver Pasha and his German military advisers decided this Russian threat had approached too close to their military nerve centres, too close to Russian cooperation from the other side of the Black Sea.

They planned to send a force against these troublesome Russians at Trebizond. We wanted the exact plan of these proposed operations.

Also the sizes of the guns in the Turkish shore forts, and what reserves of ammunition they had. While one was about it, a chart of the location of the mines in the Dardanelles might come in handy.

That was my chore.

There was no difficulty in getting to Salonica. We had open communication that far. From there I made the tedious, roundabout rail trip to Adrianople, strategic railway centre and third largest city of European Turkey.

I was not at all interested in this Oriental metropolis of mean, little, dirty, crooked streets. Nor in its noisy conglomerate of mixed races. Nor in the truly magnificent mosque left by a sixteenth century Sultan as a memorial of the heights of Turkish architecture.

Not even in the ring of fortresses frowning against the adjacent Bulgarian border. I was in the heart of Turkish territory, but still nearly 150 miles from Constantinople. The rest of the journey must be by an underground route.

As arranged, I went to the edge of the suburb of Yilderim, on the Maritza River. I met there an Armenian from Constantinople, who was in our employ.

I knew him. Each of us small spiders had by this time spun his own network of sub-agents and casual assistants, as intimate parts of the colossal international network to which the Service had grown. This fellow was shrewd and resourceful. I believed him trustworthy. It was up to him to get me across that last closed stretch.

His plan for smuggling me through the Turkish lines was simplicity itself.

Some of the finest tobacco in the world came from the Kavalla and Drama district in the coastal region of what to-day is Greek territory, east of Thessalonica. There was one fancy grade of that fine-leaf Turkish tobacco which brought export prices up to $1.75 a pound. Naturally enough, both the growing and manufacture were strict government monopolies.

A constant supply of the ordinary grades, for cigarettes and hubble-bubbles, was as necessary in

Constantinople as an uninterrupted food supply; and a stream of primitive carts brought this necessity from the growing districts to the Capital.

Daniel, my Armenian guide, had struck up acquaintance with a group of these Macedonian peasants, who had camped overnight outside of Adrianople on their leisurely progress with a convoy of the precious weed.

"You will be one of them," he explained. "I have arranged it all. You are my poor cousin who must get to the city. You are partly deaf and entirely dumb. So you will say not a word, merely make yourself inconspicuous."

It sounded all right. Dressed in garments as rough and stinking as theirs, I was introduced to the Macedonian teamsters, great, hairy, good-natured peasants, who clucked in their own dialect and looked at me pityingly when Daniel explained my infirmities.

Little as we were accustomed to consider the instruments we used (any more than we considered our own safety), I felt an extra determination that nothing must go wrong which could implicate these patient, kindly human beasts of burden.

They were like the placid oxen which drew the clumsy, creaking covered wains carrying their cargo of baled tobacco.

We were off at dawn next morning, jolting and bumping at a snail's pace over the primitive roads. If anyone wishes to drop utterly out of the world he knows, while still living and breathing, I can recommend travel in the inside of an ox-cart carrying tobacco across Turkey.

As I recall it, that journey took a full week. To-day an aeroplane would cover it in half an hour.

For my purposes, however, it was a complete success. The teamsters were incurious and let me alone. The Turkish guards had no interest in deaf mutes. Not once was my identity questioned. All I had to do was to accommodate my mind to this leisurely rhythm—and wait.

The interminable trip finally came to an end. We arrived at the city gate. The sentries passed us in without incident. I was at last on the ground where my effort must be made.

Daniel and I went at once to the house of one of his countrymen. It was he who had approached the officer from whom we hoped to obtain the campaign plans.

It was necessary for me to get in direct touch with this purveyor. The Armenian go-between arranged for a meeting of principals—about five the next afternoon in a rowboat on the Bosphorus.

Like conspirators we rowed out across the placid water. After a while I perceived we were slowly drawing up alongside another boat, in which sat a tall, slender, handsome Turkish officer with a small black mustache.

The boats came together and my oarsman held the gunwales. A few muttered words passed between the officer and my Armenian. Then they skilfully changed places. In the fading light one would have had to be watching very closely to make out what had happened. Both boats rowed idly on, a little distance apart.

The officer was a linguist and a man of the

world. He introduced himself, and came right to the point.

"I am in a position of confidence on the staff of His Excellency Enver Pasha. I have the complete plan of campaign which you want."

"That is good."

"You will wonder how an officer and a gentleman could bring himself to such an act of treachery. I must explain that."

"As you wish, Effendi."

Not that I was much interested in that somewhat personal point. But I had learned the value of understanding one's tools. Also of humoring egoisms.

"Though born an Armenian, I was educated here in Istanbul. We had friends among the ruling class, important people. I entered the army and worked hard to advance in what I felt was my career. My point of view was that of a Turkish officer—even when I saw the contemptuous brutalities permitted toward Armenians. After all, we educated city folk had little in common with those unruly peasants of Southern Armenia; and I knew there was constant secret plotting to stir up trouble by the revolutionary committees.

"Then I discovered the authorities had accepted the bloody policy of Mutagh Bey—may his descendants be accursed to the tenth generation! The soldiers were turned loose again and again in a deliberate plan of settling the problem by exterminating these rebellious dogs. I was forced to watch and give external approval to the pillage, rape and massacre of thousands of innocent men, women and children of my race.

"That made me an Armenian patriot again, instead of a Turk. For years my chief thought has been to revenge that horror."

"So that now—"

"By turning over these plans I can strike these savage oppressors from within."

"I see perfectly."

"The risk to me is terrific. I must be paid a sum proportionate to the danger."

I had a sudden desire to ask how he managed to keep those contradictory emotions sorted out in his mind—racial patriotism, revenge, his professional oath, and money. But it was no time for levity. I could only applaud a resolution so conformable to my wishes, and bargain as shrewdly as I knew how.

We agreed on a price. It was high, but the plans were worth it to us. He prepared to leave, as unobtrusively as he had come.

"I can secure everything you wish," said he. "But you must give me a few days."

"That is for you to decide."

"Like everyone else I am watched. So far I have deceived Enver's spies, but they are very clever and terribly persistent. It may be impossible to notify you in advance: you will have to be ready at a moment's notice."

I assured him I would be waiting at the Armenian's house, prepared to close at any instant he could bring the stuff, night or day.

We separated furtively.

Through shrewd Daniel I arranged with a fisherman to hold his motorboat ready for a call that would require instant action. He was told we would want to be landed in a small Rumanian port on the Black Sea. Smuggling was no novelty to this old boatman; he was keen for the job when he heard what his pay would be.

We went back to our temporary headquarters, and settled down to that hardest of all routines—waiting idly for the moment of swift action, amid unknown dangers that might pounce on us at any moment.

The Armenian's dwelling house was built around a central court of columns, palm trees, flowers and a fountain; it was flat-roofed, with the usual galleries. A pleasant enough abode under other circumstances.

As it was, all I could do was again to discharge my mind of all speculation, all thought, concentrating my powers into a complete readiness for action when the moment arrived.

Several days went by in this taut quiescence. We did not dare make the least attempt to communicate with our officer. We ate and lounged and slept in an unnatural sort of serenity amid this hostile city, unaffected for the time being by any of the currents of intrigue swirling about us.

At length, one night, I was sitting in an upper room with Daniel.

"This is slow," he complained. "As slow as those Macedonian ox-carts that brought us in."

"Never mind. When we leave this town we'll leave fast, if that's any comfort to you."

At that instant we heard rapid steps outside. We jumped to our feet as the Turkish captain rushed in.

His olive complexion was gray. His large black eyes were wild.

He had burst in downstairs where the Armenian was sitting, asking for me. "The secret police are following! Quick." "Up, fool," murmured the other, not stirring. "Up. Over the roofs. I will meet them." Now, as he found me, his whole appearance showed his terror.

He thrust a silk-rolled parcel at me.

"The money!" he demanded. "Hurry. The money—and let us fly instantly, or we are all dead men."

I hurriedly glanced at the documents and diagrams. The parcel did not contain all we had bargained for, but it was a haul. I was glad to hand him a package of notes.

Thrusting this inside his shirt, he darted out. Daniel and I got the small bundles of necessaries we had prepared, and set about our own escape.

We ran softly up to the roof, crossed it, and jumped over the parapet to the adjoining one. The officer had vanished. Our idea was to get down through the next house.

That was no go. The trap-door leading down next door was fastened from below, not to be opened.

To call would be fatal. We stole back to our own dwelling, descended the top stairway, sat down in a small room with a broken-down couch. Hands on pistols, we awaited events.

In a few moments, however, I observed that Daniel, this cheerful, resolute guide, was nervous. He ducked behind the couch in the corner, where he was completely hidden. I had expected something better, after his earlier behavior.

Meanwhile, only a few moments after the officer had arrived, a squad of police had entered downstairs. The sergeant in charge confronted the impassive Armenian owner.

"Where is the Captain?"

"What captain, Effendi?"

"The officer in Turkish uniform who entered this nest of traitors just now."

"No officer came into this room, Master. I was almost asleep, but I should have known had one entered."

"You lie, pariah dog. He came. I shall search the house. And when I find him I shall shoot you for the slinking jackal you are."

"That will be as the Master wills," replied the Armenian submissively.

The police officer hastened on through, afire with the chase.

"Search each floor," he shouted to his men. "See that not a rat escapes. I will take care of the roof and cut them off there."

Quick steps mounted. I heard doors slammed below, the frightened squeal of a woman.

The sergeant was just setting foot on the ladder-like steps to the roof when a cautious glance about showed him the open door of the room in which we were. He must have caught a glimpse of me, sitting there.

"Aha!" he called. "That is it, eh?"

Long years of bullying servile subject races had removed all thought of possible resistance to his acts. He came in, revolver drawn, but more from a sadistic pleasure in the idea of shooting down some cringing prey than from precaution.

"So here you are, little mouse–snug as possible," he roared. "Come along!" he called to the men below.

I had those documents on me. It was death if we were imprisoned. Worse, it was open, shameful failure.

I raised my right arm. "All right," I called.

The fellow advanced diagonally toward me, a most unpleasant grin on his sallow face.

He pointed his pistol directly at my stomach. That stopped my left hand, which was stealing toward the automatic in my belt.

"Aha! So we have ideas, have we? Naughty, very naughty id–"

The word broke off. Out of the tail of my eye I saw Daniel pop quietly up behind the old couch, draw a heavy knife, and throw it so expertly it sank into the sergeant's back. The man staggered, gulped, fell forward.

The other four policemen were just entering. I grabbed my gun and shot as fast as I knew how. Daniel shot too.

A minute later, the sergeant lay face down in a pool of blood. Two of the policemen were also dead. The other two, whimpering and terrified, had thrown down their weapons and were begging for their lives.

We never killed needlessly. Leaving those two alive did not much increase our danger. We tied them securely, assured them any move within the next hour would be their last. Then we left that house swiftly.

It was deep night. Daniel led the way through a maze of narrow streets. We reached the water-side without being challenged.

From a secluded spot beneath a ruined pier we

made the signal agreed upon with our fisherman-smuggler.

He was a man of his word. In a few minutes we heard the sound of oars through the blackness. We waded out to meet the skiff, stepped in, and were shortly aboard our chartered motorboat.

By this time it was nearly two in the morning. To my disgust the captain declared we must wait. The strictly enforced port regulation was that no boat of any sort could leave the harbor before daylight.

It seemed sheer madness to sit there with those fatal documents next my skin. I went to the anchor-chain locker, scrabbled rusty links aside, put my precious papers down there, and covered them over.

Then, once more, nothing for it but to wait—*without* speculating whether those bodies had been found yet, how soon the hunt would be up, when they would strike our trail.

Rarely have I looked with more pleasure at an approaching dawn than I did when the sun bobbed up out of the sea to eastward.

Dressed like the fishing crew, we fussed about the deck, tidying up the gear. The motor *put-putted.* Final miracle: it worked right away.

I was off to safety with my prize—leaving the Turkish-Armenian officer, avenging patriot or traitor, to make his own escape by his own route, with the material reward of his patriotism.

I heard later that he managed to get into the British lines at Gallipoli, where he was imprisoned. That must have seemed to him blissful safety compared with what he left behind.

From these scenes of what a westerner would call "typical Oriental intrigue," I swung back across all Europe to help attend to some not altogether admirable gentlemen claiming the same nationality as myself.

My real assignment was to break up a troublesome nest of renegades who had set up in business for themselves and, using a base in Holland, were selling bulletins of troop movements to the enemy.

On the way I had an experience which helped to increase my watchfulness even toward my own countrymen.

I had bought the plans of a new ordnance mechanism just adopted by another country. The quickest way to transmit them safely to headquarters seemed to be through one of our vice-consuls whose office was near by.

So I went to him and asked him to put the rather bulky parcel into his diplomatic pouch. To my amazement he demanded I should give him personally $500 for this. Of course I had to report such conduct. An investigation showed he had been for quite a while embezzling government funds, and he was chucked out of the service. I got my documents back through another channel; but I was quite prepared to deal rigorously with that little band of undesirables when I reached Holland.

I soon checked up on them.

They had formed a loose organization of peasant helpers, who for a pittance brought them any scraps of military information they could pick up; these bits were put together by the three conspirators (vacant places in the reports being probably filled in by their own guesses), and were sold as a regular service to the enemy agents in Rotterdam.

The scheme was clearly profitable, for the trio had taken a handsome furnished château, set up a luxurious establishment, and were living on the fat of the land.

We could only reach them by extra-legal methods. I decided on the straightforward plan of raiding the house and kidnapping all three ringleaders.

To ensure surprise, I first bought their butler. He was not too happy anyhow, since he perceived he was sharing great risks and getting none of the profits except his regular wage: he readily agreed for a good fat tip to admit me quietly a few evenings later, when the whole crew would be at home.

Enlisting two other members of our service, we drove out to the place on the appointed evening.

It was a miserable rainy night. We stopped at the big gate and walked quietly up the broad, tree-bordered avenue.

I rapped lightly on the massive door in the manner arranged—first three times, then twice, then once.

It opened almost instantly, showing the scared face of the butler in the dim light of the reception hall. We moved in silently. Without a word he pointed to the double doors on the right, and disappeared in the other direction.

His directing gesture was not necessary, for the clink of glasses and bursts of laughter from behind those dining-room doors told just where, and how wholeheartedly, these successful business men were relaxing.

Pushing the doors open I stepped in, my assistants a step behind and on either side. The three partners had been making exceeding merry with the aid of three vivacious ladies from the near-by city. There were remains of an excellent dinner amid the candles and flower decorations, full bottles of champagne on the table and empty ones on the floor. One of the girls was whirling about in a Spanish dance, with great display of silken legs.

Our unheralded entrance came as the dramatic, unexpected response to the final stamp of her high heels on the bare floor. It cut the gaiety off like a sharp knife. There was a petrified instant of silence.

Then one of the men facing us woke to the danger. He pulled out a revolver. But he was somewhat fuddled, and taken by surprise: before he could get it levelled one of my men fired. The fellow collapsed; his gun thumped to the floor; slowly he slid sideways off the chair.

"Don't move, either of you," I called sharply to the other two. They saw it was hopeless and gave up.

Assuring the women they would not be harmed if they kept quiet, I had them locked up in a little room adjoining, while we searched the place thoroughly.

We found a lot of maps and reports ready for delivery. The evidence of the spy ring's activities was conclusive. The next problem was to get them out of the country so our authorities could deal with them.

Tying and gagging them, I took them to a safe distance from the château. There I left them under guard of one of my men, while the other and I went off to make arrangements.

These took the shape of a truck and two big boxes, with which we returned in triumph. One of the rascals was deposited in each box, and these were loaded into the truck. There would be enough air to breathe, through cracks beneath the rim of the cover; we did not worry particularly over their discomfort, but drove them to town and down to the docks.

I had learned of a little Swedish tramp steamer which was sailing for a friendly port about daylight. The captain was glad of any paying freight, even of such suspicious sort as this. We hustled our boxed captives aboard.

Two days later we landed our prizes safely, and I delivered them to the proper authorities.

Both were court-martialled and shot.

I went on down to Spain on another mission, in connection with the intensified submarine campaign which the German naval staff was urging, as the one sure means to a decisive victory. We knew there was a base near Cadiz for the U-boats covering the Gibraltar section; but our people had not been able to learn where and how the Bay of Biscay fleet was being supplied and refuelled.

As a tourist, looking for a quiet place to fish and rest, I worked slowly along the coast, getting no hint of what I was after. Then, between Aviles and Gijon, I came to the little fishing village of Peñas, at the tip of the Cape de Peñas.

That looked promising. It was remote, with a minimum of connection with the outside world, and the situation seemed favorable for just such operations.

I loafed about the shore a couple of days, seeing nothing suspicious. The native fishermen were not friendly, and I had to be very casual in my inquiries.

Toward dusk of the third day I saw a big steam trawler come in. The activity which followed focussed my attention on this visitor: great steel drums, barrels, cases of provisions were being hurried aboard her.

The volume of these supplies was quite out of

place for a trawler, whose trip usually lasted only two or three days.

I turned to a grizzled old sailor lounging on the dock beside me.

"They must have a lot of big eaters aboard that boat," I remarked.

He gave me a dirty look. "What business is that of yours?"

"None whatever," I agreed cheerfully. "I was only thinking that if your Peñas air gives people such appetites, I would hardly dare to stay much longer, for it would ruin me to feed myself when I get back to Madrid."

He spat. "Needn't stay on my account," he muttered, turning away.

Feeling convinced his attitude manifested an instinctive local desire to protect a trade that was bringing money into Peñas, I telephoned our nearest embassy, suggesting that the allied patrol fleet keep a sharp watch over that stretch of coast.

Then I returned to an unobtrusive watching of the suspected trawler. When she sailed, at midnight, I was convinced we had hold of the secret.

Getting through again with my report, I was relieved to hear that a pair of destroyers were scouring that stretch of the Bay.

And next day I learned one of them had sighted the innocent fishing craft actually alongside a surfaced U-boat, busily unloading the supplies I had watched being shipped.

The trawler was sunk. I could never learn whether the submarine got away or not. There were scores of such unfinished stories in our work. Many a time we picked up loose threads of fact long afterwards, when we were deep in some quite different mission. Some sequels remained permanently hidden.

In this case I had little disposition to think over even the most exciting past incidents. For I was ordered to the United States which, still officially holding itself aloof from the vast struggle, was more and more becoming the key factor in the outcome.

CHAPTER XIII

America, Seen and Unseen

"You'd better spend most of your time in just meeting people over here at first—all sorts of people," said my superior.

I had been given a minor official status which explained my presence but did not hamper my intimate professional activities.

"Whatever you say. After all, though, I have met quite a number of people, of quite a few races, in the last ten years. Is this a new species?"

"All peoples are different. But these are more so," he remarked sententiously.

Some points of difference struck an outsider instantly. The extreme vulnerability, and lack of adequate defenses, of the great cities along the Atlantic seaboard were startling to a man who had been forced to the revealing study of "military geography." He tried to explain that to himself as a natural result of fortunate isolation and centuries of immunity from even the fear of attack. Still it didn't quite make sense.

And in 1915 the recent record of internal happenings indicated a vast carelessness, an apparent blindness to what was actually going on under the cover of "freedom," which was completely incomprehensible.

Just consider a few points in the sequence of this still unwritten history.

Four weeks after war broke out, Dr. Bernhard Dernburg arrived in New York. He announced to the newspapers:

"I have come here to make arrangements for cooperation between the Red Cross Society of Germany and that of the United States. Of course the Germans will do what they can to facilitate the work of all whose humanitarian impulses lead them to assist us in this hour of national stress."

At once he opened an office at 1153 Broadway, on the floor above the editorial rooms of *The Fatherland*, a pro-German weekly edited by George Sylvester Viereck.

In reality, of course, this organization set up

was a definite part of the imperial war machine, for espionage and propaganda in enemy and neutral countries. There was a regular board of directors: Ambassador von Bernstorff, as chairman ex-officio, exercising supreme authority; Dernburg, especially in charge of propaganda; Captain Boy-Ed, Captain Franz von Papen, Captain Hecker, Dr. Fuehr and Dr. Albert. Naturally a number of Americans were enlisted, some working because of racial sympathy, some for money. The Delbrück law of 1913 had specifically authorized a German to accept citizenship in sixteen other countries—without altering his allegiance to his Fatherland.

The workers of this group represented various departments of the German government:

(1) *The Foreign Office*, in charge of the attack along racial, religious and political lines. These operatives classed themselves far above those in other fields.

(2) *Admiralty Intelligence*, concerned with naval information, sabotage and destruction of shipping. Captain Boy-Ed, naval attaché at Wash-

ington, started this effort; he was succeeded by Naval Reserve Captain von Rintelen, who acted at times independently of the Ambassador, and whose specialties were fomenting strikes, urging the movement for an embargo against munitions shipments, and destruction of vessels by fire-bombs.

(3) *Army Intelligence*, aiming to hamper war manufactures by commercial operations, and to arrange for smuggling contraband into Germany, sometimes through neutral countries.

Funds for the heavy expenses came by wireless transfers from Germany, from the sales of German bonds, from Red Cross subscriptions.

There was plenty of money, plenty of trained enthusiasm, plenty of material to work with—and all the freedom in the world. The machine promptly began to grind. Banks, business houses, manufacturers, the hyphenated Bunds and societies were organized into a great network. Later there were probably two thousand persons acting in one concealed capacity or another.

And as the struggle in Europe became more desperate, and the tide of American opinion set more steadily against the Reich, things were done in the officially neutral United States which it seemed no country could permit—such as the paid incitements to strike addressed to foreign munitions workers, printed in foreign language newspapers.

Apparently the whole experience was so new to the United States that it was most difficult, first to believe what was going on, then to meet it adequately within the frame of their traditional ideas of free speech and action.

There were definite enough indications of these sub-surface activities.

The alert British Naval Intelligence intercepted, decoded and translated hundreds of despatches to and from Germany. Among them was this one from the Berlin Foreign Office to the German Ambassador in Washington, as it emanated from the General Staff:

"Berlin, N.W. 40, January 24, 1915
"Moltkestrasse, No. 8

"To the Foreign Office, Berlin

"With reference to A. S. 5h of the 23d inst.

"It is repectfully requested to have despatched the

following telegram in cipher to the Imperial Embassy at Washington:

'FOR MILITARY ATTACHE': PEOPLE FIT FOR SABOTAGE IN THE UNITED STATES AND CANADA CAN BE ASCERTAINED FROM THE FOLLOWING PERSONS:

1—Joseph McGarrity, 5412 Springfield, Philadelphia, Pennsylvania
2—John P. Keating, Maryland Avenue, Chicago
3—Jeremia O'Leary, Park Row, New York City

'NUMBER ONE AND TWO ABSOLUTELY RELIABLE AND DISCREET, NUMBER THREE RELIABLE, NOT ALWAYS DISCREET. PERSONS HAVE BEEN NAMED BY SIR ROGER CASEMENT. IN UNITED STATES SABOTAGE CAN REACH TO ALL KINDS OF FACTORIES FOR WAR DELIVERIES; RAILROADS DAMS AND BRIDGES MUST NOT BE TOUCHED THERE. UNDER NO CIRCUMSTANCES COMPROMISE EMBASSY, AND EQUALLY IRISH-GERMAN PROPAGANDA.'

ACTING GENERAL STAFF

(Signed) NADOLNY"

Either these limitations were removed later, or some enthusiasts could not let their imaginations be fettered by them.

Another bit of light is furnished from a paper among the secret documents published by the new régime after the Russian revolution. This was a circular telegram from the German government to its representatives:

"It is brought to your attention that in the countries where you are accredited there have been founded special bureaus for organizing propaganda in countries of the coalition at war with Germany. The propaganda will have for its aim the inception of social disturbances accompanied by strikes, revolutionary outbursts, separatist movements, and civil war, as well as an agitation in favor of disarmament and the cessation of this bloody war."

Again, there is the personal statement of Friedrich Hinsch, taken in connection with the claims for the terrific Black Tom and Kingsland explosions. He finally admitted that early in 1915 he had a conference in Baltimore with Franz Rintelen, a Marine Corps officer of the German Navy, who had been sent to the United States by the General Staff and supplied with $500,000 to pay for various kinds of destruction. In accordance with instructions received, Hinsch proceeded with various attempts to cripple munitions plants, *and to inoculate horses and cattle with anthrax and other deadly contagious diseases.*

Naturally, I am not moralizing upon these matters: such acts, and far more shocking ones, are not outside the theory of modern warfare.

Logically there is no limit to the efforts to destroy each other when two nations are at death grips. But one can surely say that the systematic logic of the theorists who develop such ideas looks rather different when put into practice, especially by the unrestrained enthusiasm of mercenaries and amateurs.

Revelations began to crop to the surface, owing to what one can only characterize as the arrogance of some of these accredited representatives—together with a queer inability to understand the psychology of other peoples, and a singularly unfortunate habit of noting down everything and preserving a full file of receipts.

Dr. Dernburg was so loud in his justification of the sinking of the *Lusitania* that he was requested to leave the country; his more important functions of propagandist and paymaster were taken over by

Dr. Heinrich Albert; while Captain Hecker announced his own succession as Red Cross Commissioner, appealing for funds which "we need more than ever"—though $1,985,000 had already been collected, and spent no one knew how.

Busy Dr. Albert soon attracted attention to himself. In fact, Washington became sufficiently curious to assign a secret service man to watch him day and night.

This operative, F. B., easily learned enough to make him determined to get proofs. He suspected there was plenty of evidence in the bulging briefcase the Doctor always carried. So one day when Albert went from Washington to his office at a fashionable New York hotel, B. followed him.

Reaching New York, Dr. Albert took his regular route uptown—Sixth Avenue Elevated to 42nd Street, then a walk across to the hotel. He sat in the L car, the briefcase beside him, musing doubtless upon the growing importance of his labors. The windows were open on this spring day. There were a number of people standing in the aisle and on the rear platform.

As the train slowed for the 34th Street station, a sudden disturbance broke out: loud voices and jostling among those standees. Then a shout, and blows. Men milling about on the rear platform of that car.

Taken by surprise, Dr. Albert jumped to his feet to see what was happening. The train was just coming to a standstill.

And at that precise instant an arm reached through the window from the station platform. A hand seized the momentarily unguarded brief-case.

When Dr. Albert sat down—the quarrel inside having subsided as swiftly as it began—this precious receptacle was gone. No explanation. No suspicious person in sight. Clearly not the work of the riotous group he had been watching. An utter mystery.

Meanwhile Agent B. was speeding away from that vicinity with his treasure-trove. Its contents made interesting reading—copies of orders, lists of assistants, receipts for expenditures, a documentary record of just what the German Commissioner had been about. There was even a garbled version of a talk between von Bernstorff and President Wilson, so full of dynamite it was never made public.

The implications of these records were so serious that the matter had to come before the President. In the difficult and strained state of American diplomacy just then he was anxious not to take official action. So he adopted an unusual course.

Calling in a newspaperman in whom he had confidence, Louis Seibold, Mr. Wilson turned over to him the complete dossier. And for the next year the secret service men gave Seibold everything they got. On this firsthand basis he wrote a series of articles, published in the New York *World*, which made a public sensation.

And so it went—one piece of evidence after another that the ardent nationalism of foreigners was operating in utter disregard of American laws and welfare. To a man of my training it was truly surprising that a great nation could tolerate such behavior. All secret services violate the laws of the lands in which they work—under the most implicit mutual understanding that they do so at their own risk. The bungler who is caught red-handed meets short shrift. Anything else seems to us unprofessional. We accept it as a maxim of hard common sense that a national government's first duty is to protect its own existence—which involves the stern repression of those who conspire against its peace.

However, this incredible tolerance was a fact, to be accepted and worked with, however difficult it might be to understand.

And as I got more familiar with the inside workings of this mighty machine, I soon perceived that my former realistic education in the average man's motivations was as serviceable as ever.

In order to make my special knowledge of most benefit, I was loaned to one of the chief allied countries, as an inspector of munitions.

Every American factory capable of it was turning out guns, ammunition and war supplies for Europe, to an aggregate of not millions but billions of dollars. And another of those bald facts one must face is the black magic exercised upon humans who come near vast flows of money. Common prudence demands the most careful checking and supervision.

What may happen without supervision was suggested vividly by the notorious case of the Russian General, who came to the United States to purchase much-needed rifles for his country's army. A shipload of guns was promptly despatched, and finally reached the hard-pressed Russian forces on the Carpathian front line—when it was discovered that these weapons were wooden dummies. The General had pocketed a million dollars, and decided to remain amid such opportunities.

My special responsibility was to inspect the ammunition feverishly produced at a great factory.

I could not help reflecting on the prices the combatants abroad were paying: shells for which the maker was paid $20 a thousand were sold to Europe at $47, plus a heavy interest on money advanced; rifles costing $8 were charged at $19.

That was none of my business. But I realized the need for vigilance when I perceived that practically every foreman in this works was either German or Austrian. Probably that had come about merely because the technical requirements brought trained men of those nationalities into such jobs; but it would be too naive to doubt that among these there would be some whose racial sympathies would lead them to sabotage. The most scrupulous man who retained those deep race sentiments would be under terrific temptation at finding himself employed in turning out deadly missiles for use against his countrymen.

I adopted the most careful system of inspection, regardless of my own hours or the convenience of others. And it was not long before these precautions justified themselves.

Testing a sample lot of cartridges, I found they would not fire at all. Sawdust had been substituted for powder.

I held up an entire shipment valued at $600,000. While superintendents and managers raved, I went through that lot with a fine-tooth comb. More sawdust. Bullets all out of shape. Some ingenious specimens that were calculated to blow back into the rifleman's face when fired.

I could do nothing except condemn the whole shipment.

That emergency brought the big guns into action. A smooth gentleman, claiming to represent the management, came to see me. He admitted there might be a few defective shells: that was bound to happen. They had taken steps already to prevent any recurrence. Meanwhile the delay would be most serious to Allied commands who were ever urging more speed in shipments. Did I not really think . . . ?

At length, seeing these arguments were futile, he flatly offered me a check for $100,000 to O.K. the shipment.

That struck me as being slightly lacking in the acumen with which American big business is credited. Whatever we are or aren't in our service, we don't sell out our own people. And if I had been such a person, I should have been singularly stupid to accept payment in so incriminating a form.

I took the cheque—and tore off the portion containing the amount and signature, putting this in my pocket.

There was a terrific row. The management got their chief owners to complain to the mission I represented. I was utterly unreasonable. I must be instantly dismissed if they were to fill orders speedily.

Of course that got nowhere. My superior knew me and had my report. He did not even have to be so tactless as to mention that foolish attempt at bribery.

When that inspection need slackened, I returned to my own proper task. Here was all this buzzing activity of enemy espionage and sabotage, almost unchecked. Wasteful as the method seemed, an alert operative might produce occasionally evidence of acts and plans which would demand action by some official in that complex network of Federal, State and local authorities. It was for me to dig out proof, and bring it to the attention of anybody who would and could work with me.

I had no official standing in such matters. Better for me to make my own connections—by demonstration. It made no difference to us whether an official was moved to activity by plain sense of duty, high patriotism or a receptivity for publicity. The first principle was to get something which could not be ignored.

I brought over from the Continent a woman sub-agent whom I had tested thoroughly, and who had some special qualifications for this problem.

As a rule I dislike using women helpers. I confess freely I have little understanding of women. But I can learn from bitter experience. And the two narrow escapes where I came nearest to open, shameful exposure were both due to women—one an ingenuous member of my own family, the other a woman I had every reason to trust implicitly. I could never forget those humiliations.

Outside of those personal misadventures, women seem to me unreliable in my craft. Up to a certain point they may succeed magnificently. Then, at a crisis, they go to pieces from some inner emotional reason incomprehensible to a man.

Miss O. was to me what William James used to call "the one white crow that proves all crows are not black." She was as far as possible removed from the showy sirens so beloved by spy-story writers. Indeed, there are quite obvious disadvantages for secret service in those dazzling ladies, fit to enthrall millions on the screen, liable to stop traffic anywhere. Anyone who noticed Miss O. at all would probably have classified her as a school teacher in a small town, or one of those superior farm wives common in America. Even in casual conversation she was, purposely, a quite colorless, unremarkable person.

As a matter of fact, beneath this commonplace exterior, there lay a quite remarkable intelligence. Born in the United States, she had lived much abroad. She was familiar with several languages, her brain was alert, her curiosity boundless, and she had a quiet way of getting results which made her invaluable.

I instructed her to begin at once to make friends among the German-Americans in New York, and somehow to get into the confidence of the group which had for years loudly attacked the idea of assimilation into the American ideal. The president of the powerful Deutsch-Amerikanischer Bund (German-American Alliance) which at one time had 10,000 local societies, arrogantly voiced this sentiment:

"We have long suffered the preachment that 'you Germans must allow yourselves to be assimilated. You must merge with the American people.' But no one will ever find us prepared to descend to an inferior Kultur!"

And a writer for the *Alldeutsch Blätter* declared:

"It is the duty of everyone who loves languages to see that the future language spoken in America shall be German."

These extremists boasted of the political power of their two million members and raised money "to combat nativistic efforts." When 1914 came, there was no question where their sympathies lay. The leaders burned with ambition to strike some shrewd blow for the Fatherland, which might even come to the attention of his All-Mighty Imperial Majesty. The Bund leader proudly wore the Kaiser's decoration of the Fourth Order of the Red Eagle, didn't he?

Miss O.'s name has a Teutonic sound. She was just back from the war zone, and was full of first-hand observation, and optimistic details of German success. She was heartily welcomed by the families to whom she had brought letters.

When her position was thoroughly established, she selected one of the ladies whom she found most sympathetic to the idea of non-assimilation, and soon became intimate with her. They lunched and dined together, talked confidentially, speculated on various matters it was becoming unwise to discuss openly.

One day, in a burst of confidence, Miss O. revealed her deep ambition to do something in America for the Fatherland against which an ignorant and envious world had arrayed itself.

Her friend was delighted, but cautious.

"I myself know nothing," she whispered. "But I can put you in touch with a marvelous woman. She is at the heart of everything."

She was as good as her word. In another week Miss O. was in the confidence of a feminine leader of one active group.

She was unusually solemn when she reported to me at a private place, away even from my inconspicuous little office.

"I'm almost afraid of that woman," she said. "She looks like something drawn by Gustave Doré or Heinrich Kley."

"What do you mean?"

"She is a monstrosity. Imagine a little, crippled, deformed body in a wheel-chair. Put on top of it a huge head, with a face terrible in its ugliness. You know all that is there—but you see only a broad forehead and great dark eyes where sits a profound, cold intelligence. And even that amazing intelligence is somehow evil."

"My dear child, you are becoming as truly melodramatic as a writer of popular thrillers and mystery stories."

"You haven't seen her. When I'm with her I feel as if I were in some bad dream."

"But she is really important?"

"Her husband is a nonentity, but her brother is a millionaire hyphenate in the Middle West. Both brother and sister are fanatics in their cause. Her money and brains have made her a centre of all the plotting in this section."

"And you have her confidence?"

"I think so. She professes to believe my fervent expressions of sympathy. She hints there will be an important mission presently which they might entrust to me."

"Admirable. Carry on."

She shook her head. "It may work. And of course I'll do my best. But that woman makes my blood run cold."

Shortly after, she reported Mrs. S. had decided she had better meet the head of the German mission in person. Presumably she was to be looked over before being accepted for this hinted task.

That idea miscarried.

"I went to the house uptown as instructed," said Miss O. "When the bell rang, Mrs. S. sent me into another room while she received the great man. But evidently she had failed to warn him of her plan. I heard whispers in there. Then a man's angry voice exclaimed: 'You are mad. I cannot do that, I. Go ahead if you wish.' There were hasty steps. The front door slammed."

"A cautious Chief. Did that upset the plan?"

"That woman has a weakness—her arrogant pride. She was angry at having her arrangements upset. Consultation was unnecessary anyhow, she declared. I am to go abroad with some cipher despatches next week."

"What is the route?"

"Italian steamer to Genoa. Then through Switzerland to Germany."

"And this cipher message?"

"It will be written in invisible ink on the lining of my corset."

I laughed. "That is the feminine touch one might expect. All right. Follow the plan exactly. I will take care of everything."

"I will. But while I trust you implicitly, Captain, I hope—"

"You would a little prefer that fearsome lady should never know your part in this, eh?"

"Exactly."

"Calm your mind. You have already shown you

are cleverer than she. Nobody will know anything."

It was simple enough. A German agent escorted Miss O. to the boat. She sailed, wearing her cipher message—and simply disappeared.

What happened was that by arrangement she was taken into custody at Sandy Hook and sent back by the pilot boat. The despatch, giving some rather important information, was deciphered and handed to the proper authorities.

Mrs. S. received a hint that her activities would get her into serious trouble; her brother was interned in Oglethorpe. Miss O. reappeared after a while with a whispered tale of police brutality. There still seemed to be no suspicion of her.

There are many tales of those throbbing years which would be news to most Americans. A picturesque collection by itself would be those of the work among the foreign language groups—like the particularly brilliant organizing job of the Sokols and other traditional societies by a Czech who was taken into the Army Intelligence.

A single instance, from a man on the inside, oc-

curred when Boy-Ed and vo
quested to leave the country be
terranean activities.

The heads of that Washington
man service never knew that th
Bohemian secretary working fo
planted there by this Czech ca
have known, but did not care, th
tain on their staff was making
while she was secretly reporting a
to her service.

The explosion came. The spie
denly. There was a collection of
taining all the details of the plot
Welland Canal, which the lovely
not yet had a chance to abstract

She helped her flurried superi
their files in big wooden boxes, b
note mentally the one containing
dossier.

The boxes went to the steamer,
departing spy chiefs. At the insiste

cial captain, the charming secretary went down to bid him farewell.

Sitting down on this special box in one of the staterooms, she went through the sad process of leave-taking; and, at the last moment, had recourse to her make-up compact. As the captain protested his undying devotion, and urged her to follow him across the ocean, she coyly took a lipstick and drew on the side of the box two hearts pierced by an arrow.

Just before the ship sailed she informed the American agents of this touching piece of sentiment. It was all the identification needed when they descended upon the two travellers.

That box was seized—opened—and the documentary record seized. It spoke for itself.

But I am writing of my own personal experiences.

One day Miss O. risked an interview at my office.

I knew that must mean she had come upon something important and pressing.

"Do you know anything of a Dr. Richter?" she asked.

I searched the card catalog of my memory. "Richter? Yes. He was mixed up in the attempt to corner all the picric acid in this market, in order to cripple the munitions manufacture. I was told he had some connection with the Bridgeport strike. But I'm sure that is an error. I was on duty there, inspecting cartridges. Richter wasn't in that. He's a chemist, a specialist."

"Yes. He's a chemist."

"A Prussian officer, isn't he?"

"In his exuberant moments he brags of that. Even more of being a personal friend of the Kaiser."

"Well, what about him? I have heard nothing of him lately."

"He has just bought a country place 'way back in the hills of upper Westchester County."

"There is no law against that."

"No. The idea is he's going to raise Belgian hares."

"There's no accounting for tastes. It doesn't sound quite in character, does it?"

"Not in the least. He is up to something."

"If it were down in that Valhalla region where the authorities have already arrested dozens of those people . . . But away off up there. And Belgian hares! We'd better keep an eye on this Prussian doctor, turned country gentleman. Do you know that country?"

"It happens I know every foot of it. I once lived there."

"Good. Any place where you could stay without attracting attention?"

"I've already found there's a little farm, quarter of a mile down the road from the place he's bought. It has an old house. Nobody would think anything if I moved in there to run the farm. I can get a hired man. Or I have a brother who could come and stay a few weeks."

"Take the place at once. If you can't rent it, buy it. Better be established there when the Doctor moves in."

She obeyed orders promptly. When Dr. Richter

arrived to start his Belgian hare industry, she was in the old farmhouse on the second place from his, apparently as much at home as if she had been there from birth, doing her own work like all the other farm women of the neighborhood. A hired man, who came by the day, was puttering about the garden, stable, and a neglected potato field. Her coming had apparently not made a ripple in the self-contained calm of Stony Street.

Oddly enough, the Doctor's arrival did not attract any attention either.

The collaborating writer of these experiences was in that neighborhood recently, eighteen years after the event. The newspaper editor in the large town six miles away had never heard the name. People in the village of Shrub Oak, only a mile distant, knew nothing of a German, a doctor, or a Belgian hare farm! Finally one ancient aroused from slumber on his porch, declared he had lived all his life on Stony Street—and no such thing could have happened without his knowledge. He did finally recall there had been for a time a queer, "proud, wild feller" walking along the road. So much for reputed country inquisitiveness. The Doctor had chosen well.

Certainly, the tale seemed impossibly melodramatic when the house itself was at last located: a charming home of cultivated people: one sat in a delightful garden, where rare sedums flouished between the rocks; giant red lilies towered beside a gurgling brook and pool—home of ruminative bullfrogs; off to the east stretched a peaceful countryside; while questions and friendly answers presently revealed the hostess's lively interest in the truth behind the rumors acquired with her country home.

It was then, as now, a perfect setting for one who desires quiet. Miss O. could do little except keep open eyes and ears, and wait for some chance.

Luck has a way of singling out people who show foresight and good judgment.

Her observations were producing little—when one day the Doctor stalked up to her front door.

He explained condescendingly to the flustered, aproned housewife that the stupid telephone people, curse them, had failed in their promise.

Such a country! Could he use the lady's telephone for a distance call? He would, of course, pay the charges.

The lady was willing—and retired to a kitchen closet from which she could hear all said at his end. He barked out a number, scolded central for delay, finally got his connection. Then, speaking in German—which he evidently assumed none of these dumbhead aborigines could possibly understand—he made his communication in a series of numbers. Miss O. could not hear the answer. In tones of command, he continued in this numerical code.

Having finished, he inquired about the charges and looked up his involuntary hostess in the kitchen where she was busily peeling potatoes while a stew-pan bubbled on the stove. He explained, casually, that the Belgian hares were only a sideline: what he really was engaged in was the manufacture of fruit flavoring extracts. It was outrageous that a business man's time should be wasted by an inefficient telephone company, and that he should have to trouble a neighbor.

On being assured quietly by Miss O. that it was

all right, and he could come again if necessary, he strode off.

Presently it became evident that in addition to the Austrian gardener who looked after his place there was a Mrs. H. who formed part of the Doctor's household from time to time. I had discovered that from my end. The lady was the wife of a German business man in New York, who was on my list. She was the channel through which came the Doctor's payments—personal as well as financial payments, I was assured.

Also, as a result of most cautious investigation I had a vague notion of what the Doctor's real activities must be. It seemed hardly possible. I felt we must have something more definite before I set any wheels in motion.

Twice more Dr. Richter came to use the telephone as before. The second time he mentioned the fact that one of his brood hares had suddenly died the previous night.

It was no proof of anything, but Miss O.'s mind instantly clicked! A suggestion of the truth came to her. But it still seemed to me too vague, too impossible.

I had her telephone the Sheriff at the county seat. She explained there was a German in the neighborhood who was acting suspiciously. After communicating with Washington, the Sheriff instructed her to continue her observations, and to listen in on the telephone, now installed in the Doctor's house, whenever there was a call between him and New York, especially if the call was to Mrs. H.

This authorized eavesdropping was arranged with the local telephone operator. But the information gained in this way amounted to little. It seemed as if we had given the Doctor enough rope: I took measures for more direct action.

Securing a proper authorization, I waited until I had word that both the Doctor and Mrs. H. were at the house. According to the usual schedule that meant they would be together there another day or two, anyhow.

In response to my summons a party of thirty or forty troopers of the Sheriff's Emergency Force, under Captain Carpenter, set out from the county seat. They traveled across country, leaping stone walls and fences where necessary, to avoid notice, and arrived on the ridge back of Miss O.'s house late in the afternoon.

The officers entered the house from the rear to confer with her.

Just then a woman ran up the road, and hurried to the front door. As it opened, she was astonished to be confronted by a uniformed trooper.

"What did you want, Madam?"

"Oh! I didn't know what was happening. From my porch there I saw men riding along the ridge and down the hill. So I ran over to warn Miss O."

"I see. Well, everything is all right. But I must ask you to come and stay here for a while. And please be absolutely quiet."

The flustered neighbor obeyed. The party went quietly up the road on foot and surrounded the suspected house. The Captain and lieutenant went forward.

Gus, the gardener and handyman, came around the corner as they approached in the dusk. Calling out excitedly, he fumbled for a pistol he was carrying, but the troopers seized and disarmed him.

Turning him over to a guard they entered the house—to find the birds had flown the day before! Either something unusual had come up, or they had become suspicious.

The Austrian was brought in. Surly at first, he realized soon he must talk to save himself.

"Where is the Doctor?"

"How do I know? He is boss. He go, that is all I know."

"Where is Mrs. H.?"

"You tink I can ask? She go first. Then Doctor, he go."

That fact seemed to open a possible chance. If these two had left separately, the woman might perhaps be lured back; and she would almost certainly know where the Doctor could be found.

So the trap was set.

Next day, the thoroughly frightened gardener still insisting that he did not know how to call the lady, that she always did the calling from New

York, Miss O. was listening in when Mrs. H. telephoned from the city.

The lieutenant answered, giving a masterly imitation of Gus's guttural and broken English.

"Where is the Doctor? Get him to the telephone!"

"Nod here! Doctor go, soon after you go."

"Gone! What do you mean? Where did he go?"

"I know noddings. But must be some moneys quick."

"What do you need money for?"

"Feeds for schickens. Feed man say no money, no feed. Bill no paid. Doctor give me no money."

"Who did the Doctor go away with?"

"I nod know. A stout gentleman. But must get money right now."

There was a moment's silence at the other end. Evidently she was thinking hard. She would not want any talk in the village about unpaid bills which might attract attention. At length:

"You are a dumbhead. I will come to-day and bring some money. If the Doctor returns, tell him to wait."

"Gut. I be sure dell him."

"You bet I'll tell him," murmured the lieutenant as he hung up the instrument.

There followed a period of suspense. At last a car drove in. A striking-looking, well-dressed woman jumped out and hurried to the front door.

"Gus!" she called angrily. "Gus! Where are you, stupid fool?"

She was petrified when she saw the officer appear from the dining room.

"Madam," he said gravely, "Gus is unable to come at present. But we must ask you some questions."

"What do you mean?" she stormed. "Who are you? And what are you doing here? I will have you arrested!"

"If an arrest is made, Madam, it is not I who will be taken in charge. Where is Dr. Richter?"

"I have no idea. How should I know that?"

"We have plenty of evidence that you do know. I shall be forced to detain you until you give us the information."

"Even if I knew, I would never tell you!"

"Never is a long time. We will see if, on reflection, you cannot shorten it somewhat. Meanwhile, I regret to say you will have to put up with the presence of one of us continuously."

"If anything could make me tell, it would be that," she flashed out. "But you are wasting your time."

"Perhaps, but we are in no hurry."

For hours she held out. Fearing she might escape, or somehow send a message, one of the questioners stayed close beside her every moment. Even an angry demand that she be left alone to go to the bathroom was refused, with apologies for the necessity.

She finally broke under this calm, inevitable persistence.

"Brutes that you are, I will tell you. Dr. Richter stops at this address in New York City. And much good may it do you," she muttered. "Now let me go."

But if she counted on sending a warning, she miscalculated. She was detained while the officer got on the wire. Not till a message was received that the Doctor was actually at the given address, and had been taken into custody, was she released.

The house and adjoining workshop were searched thoroughly. The Doctor had manufactured fruit flavoring extracts: many bottles of the finished product were there, and at least one was quite innocent. (For after this ill-omened house had been transformed into the home referred to, the owners were horrified to find that a thrifty servant had found one of these bottles—and used the contents! But there were no ill effects.)

But he had made other things besides fruit extracts.

The officer and I had the same idea when we inspected the cluttered-up bottling-room. We looked all about, behind rows of innocent bottles, in table drawers, everywhere.

At last our gaze settled upon an inconspicuous box on the shelf, in appearance as innocent as all the rest.

It was locked.

Very carefully we wrenched up the lid. And then we looked significantly at each other.

Inside, packed in cotton, were a number of tightly stoppered test-tubes.

"Ah, yes," I murmured. "Unusual furnishing for either the fruit-flavoring or the Belgian hare industry."

"Quite," he remarked crisply. "I think an expert analysis of these might be interesting."

We bore those test-tubes away with a little more care than if they had contained nitroglycerine.

The report from the biological chemist was interesting enough.

Those little glass tubes contained enough cultures of deadly disease germs—influenza, typhoid and cholera—to start devastating epidemics all over the country!

I cannot prove that this man actually used these diabolical weapons to cause or spread outbreaks of disease.

But anyone who lived through those war days remembers the frightful scourge of influenza which broke out in military camps and elsewhere some time later. It came in three successive waves, becoming progressively more fatal. The records show that the first outbreak in the Central Empires was some months later than its appearance here and in the Allied countries.

By the end of September there were tens of thousands of cases. The troopship *Leviathan* arrived at Brest, October 7th, with 85 dead, 6 dying, 366 pneumonia patients, 567 influenza patients.

When the scourge had passed it had killed between eight and ten thousand young Americans in the potential drafted army.

Those mere dates seem to open up vistas of probabilities.

Also common sense searches in vain for any plausible reason why that deadly collection should have been stored in the remote country home of a chemist, engaged in manufacturing fruit flavorings and raising Belgian hares, within a few miles of a military camp at Peekskill. Unless . . . !

And finally we have the admission of an accredited German agent, that one of his jobs was to start epidemics of anthrax and other plagues among horses and cattle.

Any man is entitled to draw his own conclusions.

The conclusion drawn by the American government was to confine the Doctor in a prison camp at Oglethorpe for the duration of the war.

Then, contrary to the custom in other cases, he was deported.

I suppose there is no other country in the world where he would not have been summarily executed. But the fact seems to be that not a single spy or saboteur was shot in the United States during the World War.

Doubtless, the consciousness of strength produces mercy in government as well as individuals.

CHAPTER XIV

THE GREATEST FEAT OF WAR INTELLIGENCE

IT MAY BE BECAUSE I KNOW MORE ABOUT them—but I confess to a belief that there has never been a finer group of expert workers than the men in my own organization. Their record will compare with that of the services of any of the greatest Powers.

Yet if I had to select the most brilliant feat of the Great War, it would probably be a coup of the American Army Intelligence.

This is the more remarkable since, while the Navy had an active service, the U. S. Army had almost nothing in the way of a modern intelligence organization when the conflict broke. One was set up under Colonel (afterwards Major-General) R. H. Van Deman and speedily became a highly efficient force, working in close cooperation with Naval Intelligence, the Federal Bureau of Investigation, the Department of Justice, and the police forces of practically all the larger cities.

Their home operations were concerned chiefly with counter-espionage and protection against sabotage and propaganda; but in the active war zone their agents proved their mettle many times.

This particular incredible adventure came at the crisis of the interminable struggle on the Western Front. If any one thing could be called decisive, the results were a decisive factor in the Allied victory.

In March, 1918, the Allied cause looked gloomy enough. Russia was out of it. America for all her prodigious preparation had actually gotten less than half a million men to the front. And now Germany, faced with the certainty that it was now or never for her, had launched the smashing "Michael" operation toward Amiens, seriously crippling the British, almost breaking the French at the Marne. A huge further offensive was clearly in Ludendorff's mind. Directed at Reims? At Flanders? At Verdun? Foch could get no definite facts of the plan. Meanwhile, at any moment the blow might fall.

Some of the best French spies had tried to get into Germany, via Holland and Belgium, to secure this vital information—only to be captured and shot.

In this emergency the Allied Council accepted an offer of the American High Command to have some of their men make the attempt through Spain.

The centre of the German espionage system was at San Sebastian, directed by a group known as the Big Five. If a man could get on the inside there . . . !

Captain Y. was selected. He had a brilliant record. He spoke German and Spanish fluently. I fancy his superior looked on him as a doomed man when he left on that desperate attempt. But there is always a chance for the determined man; and success would be colossal.

The situation was complicated by a recent extraordinary incident which was to assume definitive importance in Y.'s foolhardy attempt.

There had been a series of disastrous and alarming fires among the huge supply warehouses and gasoline depots near one of the prison camps in southwestern France; and the counter-espionage soon fastened the responsibility on a German Red Cross officer, who had the privilege of visiting his imprisoned countrymen professionally. It was proved beyond a doubt that he had distributed certain inflammable chemicals to prisoners, who had carried out this dangerous incendiary sabotage.

The Red Cross officer was arrested. Under examination his passport proved false: the court-martial sentenced him to death.

Then the American Intelligence came forward with evidence that the unimportant spy about to be erased was in reality Prince Joachim, youngest son of the Kaiser!

The High Command still insisted he must be shot, whoever he was. And he was in close custody, awaiting the order for a firing squad, when Y. started on his Spanish mission.

The American reached San Sebastian, and lost no time in approaching the German Big Five, who did business with an openness that expressed their confidence of immunity.

He explained that his racial ancestry had not been able to stand the strain: he was a deserter from the American Army. He was now determined to aid his own people. And he had, and could secure, priceless information.

He was good, that one. Those German Intelligence chiefs were far from fools, but they swallowed his story whole. After putting him through some rigorous tests, they accepted him as a valuable recruit, and took him into their confidence.

There was one final test. If he could succeed in that, he would at one bound reach a position of power in the German secret service.

And that was . . . ?

To free Prince Joachim. It was unthinkable that the Emperor's own son should meet the fate of an obscure spy. His place of confinement was only 300 miles from the border; Y.'s former position of confidence in the American Army gave him the inside facts needed for working out a plan of escape; all the resources of the Big Five's organization would be at his disposal when once he had the Prince on Spanish soil; the whole set-up was ideal. Never had a neophyte had such a glorious opportunity.

The resourceful American, already gambling with death, resolved upon all or nothing: as the savior of Royalty any door might open to him. Once in Germany, with that passport to official confidence, and his chances of success would be increased a hundredfold.

He accepted the assignment, stipulating that he was to have an absolutely free hand. He was taking all the risks; he alone knew the psychology of his former associates. Also he shrewdly diverted natural suspicion by demanding a thumping big allowance for expenses, and a fat money reward if he succeeded.

The Big Five had nothing to lose by the attempt, and much to gain. They agreed to everything. Expedited by both sides, Y. was presently back in France—giving orders to his own astonished superiors.

Through one set of underground connections he

got word to the condemned Prince to follow exact instructions on a certain day; through a private understanding with his own people, the officer of the guard in the prison camp received instructions that at a certain moment late that afternoon the sentry at the west gate was to be called away from his post for a few moments. Y. himself would be outside that gate in a fast car.

Everything went as smoothly as if the comedy had been rehearsed for weeks.

Prince Joachim, taking his daily walk, found himself close to the west gate—with no sentry in sight. He slipped through, and stepped into the rescue car. Y. stepped on the gas. They slid away into the gathering darkness. A few hours later they were across the border at Hendaye, safe in neutral Spain.

Next morning there was a triumphal breakfast celebration at the hotel in San Sebastian. The five German agents saw themselves congratulated and decorated for having engineered this brilliant coup; nothing was too good for the unknown subordinate who had helped to bring it about.

Y. played his ace of trumps. He must accompany the Prince back to Germany. While engineering the escape, he had secured information of the Allied plans so important that it must go direct to the Great General Staff.

That was simple enough. There was regular mail service by submarine from San Sebastian to Kiel. Spurred on by Y.'s insistence on the need for haste, the Big Five gave orders. The Prince and Y. embarked on the next U-boat.

It was a most uncomfortable trip, but Y. paid little attention to the cramped quarters, foul air and momentary expectation of disaster from a depth bomb or underwater net. A succession of miracles had opened one door after another. It was impossible to plan anything ahead. All a stout-hearted gambler could do was to ride his luck to the limit, and hope the incredible run would continue.

There were no doubts in Prince Joachim's mind. Snatched from ignominious death at the last moment, he was naturally overflowing with gratitude for the man who had saved him. When they reached Kiel, the Prince took his new friend with him and presented him to the commanding General, urging that he be treated with the distinction his feat deserved.

Y. found himself installed in luxury at the best hotel, while the report went to Grand Headquarters, asking if he should be sent along to lay his data before the Staff.

Then the plot developed a twist so familiar that only fact would dare to employ it.

During this necessary wait, the American had only to accept whatever he wanted. He was entertained, treated like a guest of importance. There seemed to be not the slightest limitation on his freedom of action.

He noticed a charming woman at the hotel. She was so beautiful and vivacious a man could not help singling her out. Their glances chanced to meet as both smiled over the little scene made in the dining-room by a fussy, pompous, fat business man.

Within twenty-four hours they were acquainted. And so skilful had been the manipulation that Y. was hardly sure whether she or he had taken the initiative.

She was really a rare creature. In ordinary circumstances any normal man might well have gone off the deep end for her. But the audacious spy was under the shadow of imminent failure and death at any moment—which is very steadying to the emotions. Besides there was a "pricking in his thumbs." Instinct and reason told him this was a characteristic, cold final test by suspicious adversaries, uninfluenced by royal gratitude or the decision of enthusiastic subordinates.

This woman, who made a man's pulses beat so, must be a spy.

He faced that fact—and proceeded to use it as boldly as he had all the preceding ones. It was far from difficult to pretend that he was swept off his feet by sudden passion.

That was precisely what the lady had planned, what she knew must happen when she exerted her fascinations. But Y. was so convincing—and himself so dashingly attractive—that she fell into her own snare. It was she who became infatuated.

Womanlike, she surrendered completely. She told him the whole truth. She had been planted there to ensnare him. The secret service wished her to secure something, anything, which could be twisted into justification of what they designed: to put him before a firing squad—after they had sucked him dry.

In a dramatic outburst she announced that now for her everything was completely changed. She loved him. She was determined to save him.

I can imagine what was going on inside that American as, preserving his external calm, he asked how this could be done.

And then came the climax—proving once more that when Luck fights for a man there are no limits to her favors.

There were two Colonels of the High Command, she declared. She knew them both intimately. They realized their country's cause was hopeless, especially since the failure of a complete breaking through on the last great offensive. They saw the rising flood of American reinforcements as the inevitable end of the long stalemate.

The Allies must win. And they, intelligent men in confidential positions, were determined to anticipate the debacle.

For a price, and a safe asylum in the United States they would turn over the exact plans upon which Ludendorff in a few weeks would be basing his final decisive effort.

The very thing which had started Y. on this whole mad venture! Handed to him on a platter! Because of a love affair!

My long years of experience would convince me of the episode's truth from that one impossible happening alone. It was too absurd to be anything but fact.

The gambler's luck held to the end. The two Colonels were men of authority. In an official car the party crossed the lines near Metz, crawled through no man's land at night, reached the American lines without being shot, and were taken before the officer commanding that sector.

He sped them on to General Foch. And that hard-pressed Commander-in-Chief suddenly found himself in possession of the whole detailed enemy plan of attack, uncertainty about which had been causing him such agonizing concern.

I don't hesitate to say that beautiful, beautiful job of Y.'s "won the War."

And there is confirmation of this apparently extravagant statement in the military history of those campaigns written later by Lieutenant-Colonel Wolfgang Foerster, who was at the time Chief of Staff of the German Eleventh Corps.

He describes minutely the situation and strategy, tells how the date of the final onslaught had to be put forward to July 15th. "Once more," he says, "the execution depended on surprise." But "through carelessness and treachery the German plans became known to Foch to a great extent during the first half of July."

What happened is history. Foch was able to make effective preparations. The attack came to a standstill. It was Germany's ultimate, exhausting effort. Three days later came the counterstroke—the Allied offensive at Soissons, the sweeping and astonishing effect of which is recorded by Chancellor Von Hertling: "On the 18th, even the most optimistic among us understood all was lost."

So it was. There followed the Second Battle of the Marne—then, inevitably, German collapse. The end came.

On July 22, 1919, the New York *Times* chronicled on page 1 the arrival of the transport *Agamemnon*, with 5,518 returning soldiers of the Fifth Division. Also two mysterious "German soldiers," held as military prisoners for their own safety, "in return for extremely valuable military information which they furnished to the American Expeditionary Forces in France."

The eager news-hounds smelt a sensational story, and exhausted themselves to get the untold facts. But they found themselves against a blank wall. General Dennis Nolan, head of Pershing's Intelligence, in whose charge these unknown Government wards were, confirmed the broad facts but would furnish no details. General Marlborough Churchill, to whom they were consigned in Washington (where he was Director of Military Intelligence), refused further information. The War

Department professed they knew nothing. The excitement necessarily died down.

And Y.'s identity is of course buried in the official secrecy of his Service.

That is our profession.

CHAPTER XV

CONCLUSION

MOST OF THE EVENTS I HAVE NARRATED took place some years ago. They are just as true to-day, just as representative. The world picture has not changed in the least. In all essentials this vast, ramified system exists as it was, and is—and ever shall be, so long as the nations envy, fear and distrust each other.

The surprising point to us underground is the public surprise, all over again, when some of these mole-like busynesses disturb the smooth surface.

During the year or so while this story was being written, hardly a week has passed without the eruption on the newspaper front pages of some international spy incident. These little explosions occurred all over the world which we somewhat smugly identify as civilized.

In 1937 the American Navy had a spy scandal: a petty officer went on trial, and was convicted of selling military secrets to Japan. Alarmist articles have appeared concerning espionage directed at the Panama Canal defenses and the Pacific Coast fortifications. For weeks the "Rubens" false passport cases attracted attention.

In March, 1938, a naturalized American of German birth was arraigned before a United States Commissioner on the charge of attempting to abstract data about a new single-place fighting plane, being manufactured for the Navy at the Seversky factory on Long Island.

As these words are being written, there is an outburst of excitement over a "huge spy ring." The Government has asked for some indictments. A mysterious Doctor Griebl, whose testimony is much desired, has disappeared, and has been arrested in Germany for attempting to land without a passport.

England had its share. A chemist and his helpers went on trial for selling such secrets as the new 14-inch gun, the new fuse for depth bombs, the new anti-tank pistol, a confidential text-book on explosives. A London correspondent's despatch was headed "Jittery Britain Seeing Spies in Every Lamppost." There was the usual "cultured, slender and trimly clad Miss X.," whose daring work over a whole year helped to get the evidence. In sentencing Glading, the leader of the guilty group, Justice Hawke expressed his scorn at such conspiracy "for the sole and vulgar motive of obtaining money."

That was in March. In May a Scotchwoman, married to a German, was convicted of stealing and selling official secrets.

France has had her usual quota of such incidents—including the arrest of two alleged Soviet agents for tapping the telephone wire of Alexander Kerensky in Paris; and half a dozen trials of spies attempting to get information on the hidden "pillboxes" along the Rhine frontier, and on the Maginot line fortifications.

In Germany it was found necessary to put out a propaganda motion picture, showing the methods of the foreign spies, who are declared to be very numerous and active—and the fate of citizens who furnish information. And at least one man was guillotined as a French spy, at dawn in the courtyard of Ploetzensee prison.

During those amazing Russian trials of scores of men formerly in places of trust, the charges of espionage and sabotage included agents from nearly every other country in the world. The latest furore was over a blanket charge against the Soviet bishops as Japanese agents.

Japan, of course, has for years had chronic spy fever. In May, 1938, an engineer of a British freighter was seized and fined for intruding on a fortified naval zone. As Count Kabayama expressed it: "Espionage is apparently a necessary social evil, with all nations participating, and each regarding the others as the greatest offenders."

And naturally in war-torn China spy episodes have been legion. There was even established in Honan an espionage school for the training of young girls in such patriotic endeavors.

There you have it. And there you will always have it, with men as they are.

If you do not like the picture, you can change

it—merely by getting people of different races to trust each other.

Meanwhile, it must be.

And there must also be, as my own small story shows, men who perform these secret tasks.

Men who finally look back on a long career of danger—with real pride in having done a craftsman's job of dirty work.

THE END